MENTAL AND EMOTIONAL HEALTH

JULIÁN MELGOSA

Pacific Press® Publishing Association
Nampa, Idaho
Oshawa, Ontario, Canada
www.pacificpress.com

Cover design by Gerald Lee Monks
Cover image by Lars Justinen
Inside design by Aaron Troia

The author assumes full responsibility for the accuracy of all facts and quotations as cited in this book.

Unless otherwise noted, all Bible verses in this book are quoted from the HOLY BIBLE, NEW INTERNATIONAL VERSION®. Copyright © 1973, 1978, 1984 by International Bible Society. Used by permission of Zondervan. All rights reserved.

Scriptures quoted from KJV are from the King James Version.

You can obtain additional copies of this book by calling toll-free 1-800-765-6955 or by visiting http://www.adventistbookcenter.com.

Library of Congress Cataloging-in-Publication Data:

Melgosa, Julián.
  Mental and emotional health / Julian Melgosa.
      p. cm.
  ISBN 13: 978-0-8163-2416-3 (pbk.)
  ISBN 10: 0-8163-2416-6 (pbk.)
  1. Emotions—Biblical teaching. 2. Emotions. 3. Mental health—Religious
aspects—Christianity. 4. Mental health. I. Title.
  BV4597.3.M45 2010
  261.8'322—dc22

                                                              2010025709

10 11 12 13 14 • 5 4 3 2 1

Dedication

To Annette, my wife and friend,
for her support in the development
of this book and for her amazing
insights in spiritual matters.

Contents

CHAPTER 1

Emotions

Our dentist had referred my nineteen-year-old son Eric to an oral surgeon, who was to extract his wisdom teeth. When I made the appointment, I was given instructions regarding how to prepare for the extraction; and on the day before the procedure, someone from the oral surgeon's office called us to remind us of every step. We did everything as prescribed—diet, medication, and water—and I agreed to remain at the clinic while the procedure was done and to stay with Eric for the following five hours.

We arrived at the oral surgeon's office early to take care of the preliminaries. Eric was given some forms to fill out, and I was left to deal with the finances. After examining my insurance card, the receptionist told me I had to pay an amount that seemed excessive to me. I asked for an explanation, thinking that there might be a problem with the insurance. "No, there's no problem at all," she said. "We just require most of the payment before we do procedures. When we've collected from your insurance company, we'll refund your money."

"Well," I replied, "I haven't come prepared because nobody told me about this. Besides, all the other dentists I've gone to have honored my insurance plan and billed me later."

"We're not like other dentists," she said. "We collect our payments this way."

I didn't want to argue, so I pulled out my credit card and handed it to her, even though I would much rather have paid with a check. Then I took a seat next to Eric in the waiting room and sat and stewed about the payment.

Their instructions were so complete—except they didn't say a word about the payment! I thought.

When I glanced at the clock and noticed that twenty-five minutes had gone by and they hadn't called for Eric yet, I looked at the receptionist. Though I hadn't said a word, she apologized. "Sorry. We're a little late, but I'll call you soon."

The clock continued to run, and another twenty minutes passed. Eric read magazines while we waited, but questions and resentments ran through my mind. *Why was it so important to take the medicine exactly two hours before the procedure if they're not going to start it on time? What would they say to me if I showed up an hour late for an appointment? This tardiness shows no respect for the patient. I'm going to complain!* I was becoming quite angry and frustrated. My heart was pounding, my jaw was clamped shut, and my fists were clenched.

I had begun preparing my speech when my cell phone rang. A colleague from work wanted to discuss some mundane matters. We ended up chatting about some personal things, and by the time we hung up, my mood had changed completely. I said to myself, "Why make a big deal about this and ruin my day?" and I sent a short prayer upward: "Lord, help me to be patient, calm, and polite."

At that moment, the receptionist said, "Eric, we're ready for you. Please come in." They were more than an hour late in starting the procedure, but I was much less upset than I had been forty-five minutes before. The waiting room seemed nicer, and the magazines interesting. As for the receptionist, well, her smile didn't seem artificial anymore, and her voice no longer sounded high-pitched and annoying. And when she apologized again for being so late, her words seemed really genuine. I felt happy.

Emotions are the spice of life; for without them, life would be absolutely bland. Emotions help us enjoy people, places, and experiences. They enable us to be passionate about our beliefs and convictions. But they can also lead us to make mistakes, to hurt people, to feel awful, and to sin. In the Christian life, emotional experiences are a way to live the great controversy between good and evil. That is why it is of utmost importance for all believers to know their emotional strengths and weaknesses and to pray at the right times and with the right choice of thoughts and attitudes to preclude negative emotions and promote positive ones.

Love, joy, trust, tenderness, empathy, happiness, and forgiveness are positive emotions. Sadness, anger, fear, disappointment, remorse, disgust, and hatred are negative emotions. Much of the therapy that takes place in the counseling room has to do with helping people to know and govern their emotions, to dispel their adverse feelings, and to harbor the positive ones in such a way as to avoid psychological pain.

People can initiate soothing emotions through religious practices—fervent prayer may be the most direct way. Reading the Bible, particularly Proverbs, Psalms, and the promises scattered through scriptures, encourages peace, tranquility, and the flow of positive emotions. Searching for stories of Bible characters who use their emotions appropriately, especially the stories that feature Jesus, can help us learn to face our emotions well.

Bible stories of negative emotions

The Bible contains several stories in which people follow their emotional impulses with bad results for themselves and those entangled in their lives. Let us look at the stories of two such biblical characters, Samson and Amnon.

Samson's biography, found in chapters 13 through 16 of the book of Judges, is packed with strong emotions.

- Samson sees a young Philistine woman. Filled with infatuation, and before he knows even her name, he decides to marry her (Judges 14:1, 2).
- When Samson realizes that his wife has revealed the answer to his riddle, he kills thirty men to obtain what he needs to pay off his bet, and then he goes to his father's house "burning with anger" (14:19).
- Next, Samson finds out that his wife has been given to another man, so he burns the entire grain crop of the Philistines. This results in the death of his wife and her father, as well as Samson's slaughter of many more Philistines (15:1–7).
- Samson kills a thousand more Philistines when his own people are about to turn him over to them (15:15).
- He falls in love with Delilah, who, in turn, manipulates his feelings to obtain the secret of his strength, which God has forbidden him to reveal (16:15–17).
- Deprived of his strength, Samson is captured by his enemies, who destroy his eyes and his dignity. And the Lord also leaves him, which, we can imagine, drops him into the depths of despair (16:21).
- Brought to a feast in a pagan temple to entertain the celebrating

Philistines, Samson manages to kill more of them in his suicidal death than he had killed through all the previous years of his life (16:30).

It is true that the Spirit of the Lord used Samson's behavioral quirks to fulfill the divine plan for the Philistines. However, Samson's reactions were full of hatred, revenge, sexual impulse, and the arrogant display of his strength. Had Samson been spiritually faithful, God would have found alternative ways of removing the enemy—ways that wouldn't have wasted the life of someone who had been set apart for God from birth. Ellen White commented that Samson's story teaches us that "the real greatness of the man is measured by the power of the feelings that he controls, not by those that control him."[1]

Another story packed with emotions wrongly handled is that of Amnon and Tamar (see 2 Samuel 13). There we find a son of David frustrated because of his desire to possess his half-sister Tamar. His frustration is so great that he becomes physically ill.

Amnon accepts a scheme proposed by his friend Jonadab, and full of passion, assaults and rapes her. But then he hates her even more intensely than he had desired her. Refusing to listen to her plea to resolve the situation, he calls his servant to drive her out of his palace by force and bolt the door after her.

Amnon may have felt not only hatred for Tamar, but also remorse for what he had done and fear because of what could happen to him. Of course, his deed also brought a great deal of emotional pain to Tamar, who was the truly innocent victim of the story; and it filled other family members with grief and hatred. Two years later, Absalom crafted a plan of revenge and had Amnon killed. David, who suffered throughout the whole sordid affair, had failed to bring Amnon to justice. He now had to endure the grief of losing his firstborn son by the hand of another of his sons.

Positive emotions in the Bible

The Bible also contains many examples of people who experienced uplifting feelings and emotions. While Jesus' disciples were talking about the revelation on the road to Emmaus, the Lord appeared to them and greeted them. Although at first they were startled and frightened, they soon experienced joy and amazement at His presence.

The lives of the first Christians were also full of positive emotions in spite of the many adversities they suffered. Acts 2:46, 47 says, "They broke bread in their homes and ate together with *glad and sincere hearts, praising God and enjoying the favor of all the people*" (emphasis added).

A woman in her fifties who had recently embraced the Adventist message joined a small church in Spain. One day as she was participating in a prayer group, she told her conversion experience. Halfway through, she was moved emotionally and became teary and had difficulty speaking. At this, a member of the group said to her, "Don't worry, those emotions will go away when you've been in the church for a while."

Not necessarily! Converted people can grow in their excitement about Jesus. Our Lord wants us to experience the highest level of positive emotions. He doesn't want us to live with the unpleasant consequences of hatred, discord, jealousy, rage, selfishness, dissension, and envy. Instead, He offers us love, joy, peace, patience, kindness, goodness, faithfulness, gentleness, and self-control (see Galatians 5:19–23).

Emotions can be utterly good or extremely bad. They are intimately related to mental and physical health. There is a long list of psychosomatic diseases—verifiable organic maladies that have their origin in emotional processes. They affect virtually every system, but most often the digestive, circulatory, respiratory, and nervous systems. Positive emotional states, such as compassion, kindness, humility, gentleness, and patience, bring about a sense of well-being, a positive outlook and an optimal relationship with God and neighbor.

Jesus' emotions

The Gospels allow us to glimpse times in Jesus' life when He showed emotion. When we read those passages, we can identify with Him and learn to endure emotional pain and to maximize positive emotions.

Compassion is perhaps the emotion we see most often in the stories of Jesus' life. For example, we see a leper approaching Jesus, falling on his knees and begging to be cleansed. The text tells us that Jesus, "filled with compassion," reached out His hand and touched the man (Mark 1:41). As soon as Jesus pronounced the words, " 'I am willing. . . . Be clean!' " the leper was clean.

Jesus was also moved by compassion when the more than four thousand people who came to hear Him went three days with little or nothing to eat (see Mark 8). Jesus was aware of their needs and wouldn't start them on their long journey home without nourishment lest they faint. So, miraculously, He provided food for them.

Jesus also expressed love, which is the supreme positive emotion, the central theme of the gospel. He showed His love for people on many occasions. He even set His love as the benchmark toward which His disciples are to aim, "These things I command you, that ye love one another" (John 15:17, KJV). The Lord loved Martha, her sister Mary, and Lazarus, and He found solace in their house at Bethany when He was tired. But He didn't restrict His love only to those who followed Him. The story of Jesus' encounter with the rich young ruler teaches us that He loves His children even when they don't obey Him. Though this young man turned away from Jesus, He "looked at him and loved him" (Mark 10:21). What a remarkable lesson to those who disdain and hate people who don't respond to their requests!

Jesus often demonstrated His affection for people through touching them. He held little children and touched diseased people—including lepers—when He healed them. Ellen White wrote that Jesus' disciples tried to prevent their Master from touching a leper; for "he who touched a leper became himself unclean."[2] But Jesus, being the source of wholeness, wasn't defiled. And by His act of touching the leper, He sent the message that ill people—even those with the worst disorders—deserve love and affection.

In addition to enjoying the pleasure of positive emotions, the Lord Jesus also endured the pain of negative ones. The prophet Isaiah used powerful language to reveal the physical and emotional pain Jesus suffered. He said Jesus was a "man of sorrows," "familiar with suffering," "despised," disdained, "smitten," "afflicted," wounded by human transgression, and bruised by human iniquity (see 53:3–5).

People tend to cry because of their own losses, but Jesus wept for the losses of others. He feels perfect sympathy and empathy for those who suffer. The Gospels tell us that Jesus grieved for those who rejected the appeals He made when He lived among them. Luke tells us that Jesus actually wept over the city of Jerusalem (Luke 19:41). He was fully aware that it would eventually be destroyed, and He wept at the suffering of its citizens. This is one of the two times Scripture says that Jesus wept. Meditating on this aspect of Jesus' ministry can lessen the emotional pain we feel.

The second instance in which Scripture specifically says that Jesus wept is in the story of Lazarus's death and resurrection. This story gives us additional information about the depth of Jesus' feeling. John 11:33 says that He "groaned in the spirit and was troubled" (KJV), or that He "was deeply moved in spirit and troubled." This is a translation of the Greek term *embrimaomai*, which appears again in verse 38, where it is translated "groaning in himself" (KJV) and "deeply moved." This is one of the most graphic pieces of biblical data telling us of Jesus' emotions when He felt the consequences of sin. Jesus' groan was probably audible. Certainly it showed the deep psychological turmoil He was feeling.

Here are some of the emotions the Savior experienced.

- *Grief and distress* (Mark 3:5). On one occasion, Jesus healed a man with a withered hand to demonstrate that people could be freed from the yoke of sin even on the Sabbath. Scripture says the Pharisees angered and distressed Jesus. They raised these emotions in Jesus because they would rather leave someone in excruciating pain than do what they could to provide relief on the Sabbath.
- *Frustration* (Mark 8:12). The Pharisees came to ask Jesus for a sign from heaven, even though they had already seen plenty of signs. This scenario raised a set of emotions that are difficult to label. The King James Version translates Jesus' reaction this way: "He sighed deeply in his spirit." We don't know exactly what Jesus felt; it may have been a mixture of anger, frustration, pity, and sorrow.
- *Indignation* (Mark 11:15–17). Jesus had come to earth specifically to be sacrificed for the sins of the world, and the animal sacrifices in the temple were meant to point to Him in His role as the Redeemer. Yet, the worshipers and temple personnel were missing this point. Passover involved the sacrifice of thousands of animals, and for many people, it had become a great business with no connection to the Messiah. So, although some don't understand Jesus' forceful behavior in clearing the temple, apparently the seriousness of the offense required a clear and strong intervention.
- *Anguish* (Matthew 26:37, 38). At Gethsemane, the Man Jesus experienced anxiety far greater than any other human being has ever experienced. Evidences of this extreme mental torment are (a) the feeling that He was about to take upon Himself all the guilt of humankind, past, present, and future; (b) His need of support from Peter, James, and John; (c) the fact that He told His disciples about His agony, saying, "My soul is overwhelmed

with sorrow to the point of death"; and (d) His request to the Father that if possible, "this cup" be taken from Him—in other words, that God's plan be changed, that Jesus be excused from what He was about to experience.

As we realize the intense emotional experiences Jesus went through, we can better bear the mental and emotional suffering that comes to us. We may also begin to understand Jesus' feelings now as well as then: is He smiling because we're behaving like His children should, or is He sad or even crying—as He did over Jerusalem—because we're not accepting Him fully?

Promises regarding adverse emotions

The concept of emotional intelligence emerged in 1995 with the publication of Daniel Goleman's book by that name, *Emotional Intelligence*. He refuted the traditional understanding of the intelligence quotient (IQ) and presented in its place a more global concept of ability—one that is now widely accepted in the field of psychology. Emotional intelligence (EI) isn't just the ability to answer standardized items and perform a number of highly precise problems under time constraints. It has to do with the mastering of our emotions so that we can achieve goals and build relationships. One of the most desirable traits is the ability to transform negative emotions into positive ones. Another helpful trait is the ability to survive the painful emotional experiences that everyone must face sooner or later.

Christianity has a lot to offer us when we're dealing with painful emotional experiences. One of the best ways we can gain help is by following the directions Jesus gave to His disciples when He was facing crucifixion and death. The passage that tells this story, John 16:20–24, is full of hope. When we're troubled, we can gain much comfort, strength, and hope by reading Jesus' words and realizing the following:

- *Life isn't always fair, but joy is on its way.* Many people who reject the Savior seem to be happy and enjoy life, while many of Jesus' followers weep and mourn. It isn't fair that cancer strikes someone who has always tried to follow the health message and that accidents take away young lives, leaving parents and siblings crushed. But Jesus promises that grief will be turned to joy.
- *The change from grief to joy won't take long.* The Lord won't allow us to suffer more than we can endure—that's a promise! People under severe emotional distress will leave their suffering behind

as quickly as the sight of a mother's precious newborn baby erases her memories of the pain of childbirth.

- *The unpleasant past will truly be forgotten.* Much of the emotional turmoil that harasses us issues from events of the past. That is why psychotherapists from some traditions labor session by session to help their clients deal with those past experiences that are still causing unhappiness. But Christ promises to wipe out that past as if it were no more.

- *We all must experience some grief.* Jesus pointed out that "now is your time of grief" (verse 22). Sin touches everyone, and suffering and death follow their course in all lives. Seldom can we see the reason for the tribulation we experience. But reason and evil aren't compatible. It suffices to know that Jesus adds, "But I will see you again and you will rejoice."

- *The joy Jesus gives lasts forever.* When Jesus returns, He will give His children a type of joy that nobody can take away and that will last for eternity—something difficult to understand, for joy as we understand it is evanescent. But we accept Jesus' statement by faith.

- *We won't need to ask Jesus for anything else.* Jesus affirms that although His disciples ask Him for all sorts of blessings, the time will come when those who love Him will want nothing, since all their needs will be fully met.

- *In the meantime, we must pray in Jesus' name.* The Lord doesn't leave His followers with nothing but a promise. He offers support today as His children face mental struggles and painful emotions. "Ask and you will receive, and your joy will be complete" (verse 24).

Whenever anger, hatred, jealousy, or anxiety oppress you, when you feel impatient, guilty, inferior, or stressed, accept Jesus' invitation. He promises the Father's help—not when He returns at the end of time, but now, if you ask in His name.

---

1. Ellen G. White, *Patriarchs and Prophets* (Mountain View, Calif.: Pacific Press®, 1958), 568.

2. White, *The Desire of Ages* (Mountain View, Calif.: Pacific Press®, 1940), 266.

CHAPTER 2

Fear and Anxiety

Our children, twenty and seventeen years old, had been born abroad and had spent most of their lives outside the United States. They needed a good overview of their country. So we set out on a road trip from the state of Washington to Washington, D.C., to visit grandparents and do some exploring along the way.

As we headed toward Grand Teton National Park, where we intended to camp for the night, we realized we wouldn't make it before dark. We spotted a Forest Service campground with very basic facilities and decided to stay there instead. There were no other campers, but the site did have numerous signs warning campers not to leave any food out to avoid attracting bears.

We ate supper and soon were ready to sleep. But the idea that bears were around grew in our minds. As a result, the night—full of wind and other noises—was long and wakeful. Nobody rested very well because of the many bears in our midst—imaginary ones, although they were real enough to spoil our night.

Fear is a very strong emotion that produces agitation at the presence of danger. Anxiety is similar in its effects, but quite different in that it is centered on future uncertainties. In other words, anxiety is fear, not of a blazing fire or a roaring earthquake that one is actually experiencing, but of things that *might* happen in the future.

Scripture mentions fear and anxiety in quite a few places. Some describe the emotional state of Bible characters; others provide reassurance ("do not be afraid") to men and women who face the unpleasant consequences of these emotions.

The words *fear, afraid, frightened,* and *terrified* occur 591 times in the New International Version of the Bible. (Some of these passages refer to "fear of the Lord," which is quite different from plain fear.) The words "do not fear" convey one of the most important messages God wants people to understand. He's interested in freeing His children from such debilitating emotions. Because He loves us, He invites us all to come to Him, submit our anxieties to Him, and experience peace. Peter tells us, "Cast all your anxiety on him because he cares for you" (1 Peter 5:7).

Part of human existence

Human beings experience fear and apprehension from the very beginning of their life. A group of researchers from the Semmelweis Medical University in Budapest and the University of Texas Medical School[1] in Houston studied the facial expression of human infants. They determined that baby girls as young as three and a half weeks old and boys four and a half weeks old exhibited fear when presented with frightening stimuli. And mere months later, the first form of anxiety appears—separation anxiety, a developmentally appropriate distress reaction that emerges in infants between six and twenty months of age. At this age, they recognize their primary caregiver/parent, are aware of their environments and the people around them, and cry when taken to a new place, introduced to a stranger, or separated from their primary caregiver.

Here is a sample of fears and anxious experiences that may occur in the coming years:

- Toddlers fear animals, darkness, and strangers.
- Preschoolers may fear many things, such as loud noises, sleeping alone, storms, losing their parents, or someone possibly hurting them. They also tend to be afraid of what is often associated with nightmares: ghosts, monsters, and witches, for example.
- Schoolchildren begin to experience apprehension and threatening perceptions involving school themes: tests, difficult assignments, grades, certain school activities, and peers who are stronger or who do better at their studies. And it is fairly common for children in the early grades to fear dying, even though they still don't have a clear understanding of what death means.
- Adolescents also face their share of situations that cause them

dread, such as being rejected by their friends, not being success-ful in sports, not developing physically (especially when their friends develop early), school failure, and so on.

- Young adults fear they won't find a suitable life partner or that they'll lose job opportunities or be laid off.
- Although adults have reached stability in many aspects of life, fears still trouble them too. They worry about their health and what would happen if they fell seriously ill. Common apprehen-sions involve finances (What if I can't pay all my bills?), family life (Will I lose my spouse? or Will my child have an accident?), and work (Will my boss listen to me? or Will I be the next to be fired?).
- The elderly also have their fears. They may be afraid of diminish-ing income, of contracting a disabling disease, of losing their spouse, of falling and breaking a bone, of being assaulted, of facing death, and of dying.

Virtually everyone in all locations and at all different stages of existence experiences fears in one form or another. Some fears are rooted in a haunt-ing past; others are about the here and now; while still others pertain to the future. Some are real, and some are imaginary. Some are truly impor-tant; some are trivial. But since the inception of sin, fear has always been present.

The beginning of fear

The man and woman who came from God's hands were perfect. They had no physical shortcomings and were perfectly balanced mentally. Be-fore their disobedience, they did not and could not experience fear or anxiety because they were fully cared for by their omnipotent Father. Fur-thermore, they hadn't observed this adverse emotion in any other crea-ture, so they didn't know that such an experience could exist. They were perfectly happy, in part because they weren't afraid or anxious. They knew that God watched over them and that they would be cared for in the fu-ture.

But things changed radically when Eve ate the forbidden fruit and gave some to Adam. The story in Genesis 3 tells of two immediate consequences of the transgression. First, their eyes were opened (verse 7), and they had, for the first time, a *general* awareness of evil as well as of good. Their innocence—their lack of knowledge of good and evil—vanished. They now knew sin and felt the consequences. They knew the *before* and the *after* of sin. What a difference!

Here's how Ellen White described their experience: "The air, which had hitherto been of a mild and uniform temperature, seemed to chill the guilty pair. The love and peace which had been theirs was gone, and in its place they felt a sense of sin, a dread of the future, a nakedness of soul."[2] Notice that the immediate result of their transgression was not lightning and thunder or anything outwardly observable. It was internal distress, a sense of guilt, a feeling of being exposed.

Second, when they heard God's footsteps, they hid behind trees (verse 8). Their hiding was a *specific* consequence, a particular behavior. We know the motive for their action, for when God called, " 'Where are you?' " Adam replied, " 'I heard you in the garden, and *I was afraid* because I was naked; so I hid' " (verses 9, 10; emphasis added). Thus, the fear of the consequences that would result from being found out, the uncertainty about what would happen next, was a clear, immediate result of sin.

Adam's and Eve's eyes were now opened. They were aware of the tension between good and evil. This made them subject to worry, dread, fear, and anxiety—emotions they hadn't experienced before. Many people declare, "Information is power," and "Knowledge opens doors." But that wasn't true of the knowledge Adam and Eve obtained by sinning. Humankind would have been better off without the "knowledge of good and evil."

In His mercy, God may at times conceal information from human beings because it would bring them too much pain. That's why, while God has revealed much to us, He keeps some things secret. "The secret things belong to the LORD our God, but the things revealed belong to us and to our children forever, that we may follow all the words of this law" (Deuteronomy 29:29).

Animals, even the most intelligent ones, are protected from excessive fear and anxiety. Only in the presence of threatening stimuli can they experience these emotions. Shortly after my wife and I took jobs at a Seventh-day Adventist school in Spain, we adopted a stray dog. The animal had followed one of the teachers from the train station all the way to her home near the school. She convinced us to take him into our home as a pet. He was a loyal friend to our family for many years.

Beni, as we named him, was an intelligent and lively dog, but he had one strange behavior: if one of us started the car, he would become noticeably distressed. He would start to bark incessantly and try to get into the car. If he wasn't allowed into the car, he would run after it when it was driven away. The first time this happened, I continued to drive on, thinking, *When I pick up speed, he'll stop following me and go back home.* But Beni continued to run full speed after the car, as if his life depended upon him catching it. I had to stop and let him in. My wife and I concluded that someone had probably abandoned Beni by dropping him off and driving away. From then on, we made sure that he was locked inside the house when someone left in the car. Even then, he would bark until the sound of the car disappeared. But as soon as the stimulus disappeared, he would go back to playing with our little daughter.

Beni's short-lived fear of abandonment contrasts strongly with the way we humans experience such fears. We worry about threatening events to come, endure them with fear, and, for a long time after them, live in fear or anxiety that they will happen again.

Examples in the Bible

The Bible contains many accounts in which people are shown displaying worry, fear, or anxiety. We'll look at three of them.

Abraham. This biblical character lived an exemplary life. We see him willingly accepting the call of God, leaving Haran, and setting out for Canaan. He displayed a great deal of faith and generosity to others, as well as living a life of steadfast obedience and closeness to God. However, after a period of intense activity (see Genesis 12–14), Abraham became afraid of what *could* happen. He must have been pondering one of those what-if thoughts about the son of the promise who hadn't come yet, when he concluded, *If I'm not given a son, Eliezer—just a servant, after all, and not even a member of my family—will become my heir.*

But "the word of the LORD came to Abram in a vision: 'Do not be *afraid*, Abram. I am your shield, your very great reward' " (Genesis 15:1; emphasis added). Then God told him directly that his heir would be his biological son, " 'a son coming from your own body' " (verse 4). In addition, God gave him a vision of the future and made a covenant specifying the land that his heirs would inhabit.

Abraham's doubts and fears must have diminished. But his relief didn't last long. Many other things happened before Isaac's birth, including Abraham's and Sarah's strange attempts to supply the son of the promise— all probably a result of Abraham's doubt, fear, and anxiety. But eventually, "Sarah became pregnant and bore a son to Abraham in his old age" (Genesis 21:2).

David. This son of Jesse is possibly the Bible character who felt the most fear. We can understand this when we remember that during much of his life, enemies were trying to kill him. When he was a young man, his predecessor on the throne, King Saul, pursued him relentlessly. Then, during his mature years, his own son Absalom sought to overthrow and kill him. And the Philistines battled against him throughout his adult life.

It is in this context that we find jewels such as Psalm 27, a song in which David tells how the Lord freed him from fear:

The Lord is my light and my salvation—
    whom shall I fear?
The Lord is the stronghold of my life—
    of whom shall I be afraid? . . .
Though an army besiege me,
    my heart will not fear;
though war break out against me,
    even then will I be confident (verses 1, 3).

David's key strategy for dealing with fear was trust in God. We see this in passages such as the following:

- He put a new song in my mouth, a hymn of praise to our God. Many will see and fear and put their trust in the Lord (Psalm 40:3).
- He [the man who fears the Lord] will have no fear of bad news; his heart is steadfast, trusting in the Lord (Psalm 112:7).
- When I am afraid, I will trust in you. In God, whose word I praise, in God I trust; I will not be afraid. What can mortal man do to me? (Psalm 56:3, 4).

Many people have claimed the wonderful promises David's words suggest. Committing some of his psalms to memory and repeating them at critical times has brought divine comfort to people who were afraid. It is said that Bishop Bashford, while on a trip to China, didn't have any option but to sleep outside because there was no room for him in the inn where he arrived late one night. He was warned of the presence of bandits and their nightly activity and found it difficult to go to sleep after saying his prayers. But the words "when I am afraid, I will trust in you" kept coming to his mind. Eventually, he said to the Lord, "There is no use for both of us to be watchful," and soon after, he fell asleep and had a good night's rest.

Early Christians. The first generation of converts to Christianity shared their possessions with each other. Their sharing wasn't limited to food, tools, utensils, objects, and money; it also included real estate. According to Acts 4, those who owned land or houses put them up for sale and brought the proceeds to the apostles. They, in turn, distributed the wealth to those in need. This system worked well, for we are told that "there were no needy persons among them" (Acts 4:34).

Scripture mentions the names of some donors, the first as an example of true generosity, and the others to show that God doesn't accept covetousness and deceit. Joseph, a Levite from Cyprus, sold a field and put the proceeds at the apostles' feet. Ananias and Sapphira, a married couple, pledged that they also would bring the proceeds from the sale of some land they owned to the apostles. However, they secretly agreed to retain some of the money for themselves. When asked about their donation, they lied, saying they had donated *all* the proceeds. And as soon as the words were out of their mouths, they died (see Acts 5).

It should be noted here that this communal system wasn't based on coercion. According to Peter, Ananias and Sapphira could have kept the land or any part or all of the money from the sale. But they had promised to donate all the proceeds to the general fund. And when they claimed to be doing do so, they were lying both to men and to God.

The Bible tells us that as a result of the deaths of Ananias and Sapphira, a *"great fear* seized the whole church and all who heard about these events" (Acts 5:11; emphasis added). It's difficult to know the nature of this fear. It may have increased awe toward God, but it may also have been that the church members were afraid of what might happen to them. Some may have schemed like Ananias and Sapphira to sell their properties, keep part of the proceeds for themselves, and bring the rest to the apostles to gain their esteem. What happened to Ananias and Sapphira no doubt caused them to change their minds.

At times fear leads to a positive outcome. A prudent amount of fear may save lives, and fear of doing evil can be beneficial. What happened to Ananias and Sapphira must have been necessary to keep the members of the early church on the right course.

Divine reassurance

Anxiety disorders include phobias of different types—panic attacks, obsessive-compulsive disorders, posttraumatic stress disorders, and generalized anxiety disorders. All of them have to do with fear, anxiety, and restlessness—sometimes for a known reason, other times for reasons un-known. Some, like panic attacks, are brief but very intense, with painful physiological symptoms (palpitations, sweating, shaking, shortness of breath, feelings of choking, chest pain, nausea, dizziness, feelings of unre-ality, fear of losing control, fear of dying, tingling sensations, and chills or hot flashes). Others, like generalized anxiety disorders, bring on months of restlessness, fatigue, irritability, tension, and sleep disturbances.

These problems aren't rare. From 9 percent to 11.3 percent of people in the general population experience phobias.[3] And generalized anxiety disorder has a one-year prevalence of 3 percent and a lifetime prevalence of 5 percent.[4] And these are just clinical cases. In addition, there are many people suffering less frequent, less severe symptoms that don't receive a diagnosis. Yet these people experience great pain because of their own or a loved one's job loss, family crisis, or serious illness.

God doesn't want men and women to suffer in this way. He wants us to hold on to His promises and trust Him in the face of fear and anxiety. At times we may need qualified psychological and medical treatment just as we need treatment for physical diseases. But in all cases, pathological or not, both the prevention and the cure of these adverse symptoms requires us to practice fervent and faithful prayer, communion with the Lord, and determination to think and to do what is right.

On several occasions, Jesus had to remind His followers to cast off their cares and maintain their trust in the Father. He said, for instance, " 'Do not let your hearts be troubled. Trust in God; trust also in me. In my Father's house are many rooms; if it were not so, I would have told you. I am going there to prepare a place for you' " (John 14:1, 2).

Notice that Jesus spoke these words after He predicted His betrayal and attempted to explain His last days on earth and His return to heaven. The apostles, although not quite clear about the meaning of all this, must have felt disturbed. That is why Jesus told them, "Do not let your hearts be troubled." He was inviting them to displace the fear in their hearts with trust in God the Father and in Jesus Himself. Then Jesus directed their attention to the kingdom of heaven, to the presence of the Father, and to a time when there will be no more pain, no more sorrow, and no more worry about the future. What a beautiful healing session! Jesus tells the painful truth of His imminent departure but immediately takes the minds of His disciples to the ultimate experience of being with Him forever!

In conclusion, another of Jesus' admonitions comes to mind: " 'Do not worry about tomorrow, for tomorrow will worry about itself. Each day has enough trouble of its own' " (Matthew 6:34). How much less mental—and physical—discomfort people would experience if they followed this advice!

My family and I had the privilege of serving as missionaries in the Philippines for more than eight years. We owe much of our knowledge and understanding of other cultures as well as much personal growth to that amazing experience.

We often observed that the Filipino people held to the belief that "tomorrow will be better." Typhoons and electrical storms are common during the rainy season, and they become particularly intense during September and October of each year, causing varying degrees of damage and sometimes taking human lives. But after the rain and wind passed, we often witnessed people who had lost their homes, saying with a smile, "Tomorrow will be better." This attitude—a part of the culture—was a great safeguard against anxiety. The Filipinos applied it to small and great things. It helped them to bear the pain of today and to avoid anxiety about tomorrow's pain, which might never materialize.

If your basic needs are being met and you aren't experiencing pain and you are safe, I invite you to thank God for your current blessings. If you're thankful about events in the past, include them in your praise too. And since you don't know what tomorrow will bring, let Jesus take care of your worries about what might happen then.

---

1. E. Nagy et al., "Different Emergence of Fear Expressions in Infant Boys and Girls," *Infant Behavior and Development* 24 (2001): 189–194.

2. Ellen G. White, *Patriarchs and Prophets,* 57.

3. American Psychiatric Association, *Diagnostic and Statistical Manual of Mental Disorders,* 4th edition (Washington, D.C.: American Psychiatric Association, 1994), 408.

4. Ibid.

CHAPTER 3

Stress

Flora was born in Florence, Italy, where she embraced the Adventist faith and met Daniel Lewis, an Adventist Albanian, who was visiting Italy.[1] They married in 1942 and remained in Italy for the remainder of World War II. In 1945, the family—which then included a little boy—decided to move to Albania because they felt compelled to share their faith with the people of that officially atheist country. They had no idea how much stress this decision would bring them.

The Albanian government, under the leadership of Enver Hoxha, arrested all religious leaders and confiscated all places of worship, transforming them into gymnasiums, warehouses, and public restrooms. Any reference to religion was banned, and many believers of all faiths were imprisoned, tortured, or placed in forced labor camps. Eventually, Hoxha proudly declared Albania as the only nation in the world where religion had disappeared.

Because of the horrible persecution the Lewises experienced in Albania, in 1950 they decided to immigrate to the United States, where Daniel had lived for several years and received his pharmaceutical training. At that time, Daniel and Flora had two children, John, seven, and Esther, three. On the night before their departure, an informant accused Daniel of being an American spy, and as a result, the whole family was arrested. Daniel and Flora were sent to different prisons, and the children were taken to an orphanage. Both parents were tortured for their faith. They only saw each other once more—eighteen months later at their trial. Flora said that Daniel's hair had gone white and all his teeth were gone. Flora was freed, and Daniel was sent back to prison, where he was tortured continually for refusing to work on the Sabbath. He died of heart failure two years later.

Flora was permitted to reunite with Esther, but John was kept in an orphanage and later transferred to a psychiatric hospital, where he died a few years later. Mother and daughter lived through extremely difficult times of harassment, which included the confiscation of money sent from abroad and denial of their right to work unless they recanted their religious beliefs, among other things.

Flora and Esther were subject to the highest levels of stress imaginable, but they survived to see times of freedom. How? They held onto their faith, consistently continued to commune with God, and read their Bibles, which they kept hidden for decades.

Stress, also known as the fight-or-flight response, is the organic reaction to intense demands or alarms—for example, a wild fire or a car approaching at great speed. But alarms don't always come in the form of physical threats. They also come as psychological stimuli—the recollection of unpleasant events, intense feelings of inadequacy, what someone says to us, feelings of guilt, or a screaming toddler. This is what most people understand by stress—the overwhelming pressure caused by hostile work conditions, a guilty conscience, relationship problems, tight finances, and the like.

When people perceive an alarming situation, a number of physiological mechanisms (neural and hormonal) take place inside them. The most notable changes include additional glucose production, more rapid breathing and circulation of the blood, muscle tension, dry mouth, slowing down of digestion, and blood vessel constriction. All of these changes in the body's processes increase the energy available to fight the stressor or to flee from it. Our stress response system is an excellent system designed by a loving Creator to enable His creatures to survive danger.

Of course, stress is good in moderate amounts because the extra measure of energy it stimulates us to produce gives us the push we need to finish up a project on time, to run and catch the bus that's about to pull away from the bus stop, or to finish the house cleaning. But if the alarm is sounding all the time, it soon becomes useless—or worse, it may cause diseases such as a gastric ulcer, an irritable colon, hypertension, atherosclerosis, angina, or myocardial infarction. It might even affect our immune system.

Stress

An experiment carried out by a group of researchers under the direction of Sheldon Cohen from Carnegie Mellon University showed that stress affects people's resistance to the common cold.[2] The levels of stress of 394 college students—all in good health—were assessed over a period of one year. The subjects were also administered a nasal spray containing five different types of common cold viruses, and they were examined daily to ascertain the presence or absence of viruses in their respiratory passages and any symptoms of colds. The researchers found that (1) viruses were present in virtually all the participants, but only one-third of them had symptoms of a cold; (2) the greater the stress levels, the greater the density of viruses and the greater the number of symptoms; (3) the subjects rated as high-stress individuals had double the probability of developing the illness; and (4) the stress effect remained significant even after removing variables such as age, exercise, diet, and the use of alcohol and tobacco.

The power of prayer

Those who have experienced closeness to Jesus know that prayer and communion with Him help people to handle life's stresses with a great deal of success. In fact, it seems that prayer can boost our defenses. Based on his analysis of more than fifty studies, Kevin Seybold reached the following conclusions about the effects of prayer and religious practices on the immune system.[3]

- Religious reflection and prayer cause a bidirectional activity between the brain and the immune system that lowers blood pressure and slows down one's heart rate and breathing. These changes are incompatible with stress, anxiety, and panic.
- Prayer and meditation produce an increase of activity in the left hemisphere of the brain, a pattern associated with the best immune responses, particularly the production of antibodies that protect us against infections.
- Prayer and religious practices also affect the central nervous system. They activate the brain's frontal lobe, balancing the activity of the autonomous nervous system, the limbic system, the hypothalamus, and the amygdala, which reduces stress. And they raise the levels of the neurotransmitters gamma-aminobutyric acid (GABA), melatonin, and serotonin, which are internally secreted chemicals that induce relaxation and inhibit anger and aggression.

- Public affirmation of one's values and beliefs reduces the level of cortisol—the stress hormone.
- Religious practices stimulate the production of dopamine as well as the activity of the prefrontal lobe—the part of the brain involved in making moral judgment, controlling impulses, and making decisions. This explains why religious practices, when perceived as positive, tend to perpetuate themselves.

One prayer that Elijah prayed probably didn't bring about the benefits listed above. This particular prayer was an unusual one, which Elijah prayed after a great deal of physical, emotional, and spiritual commotion. He pleaded, "I've had enough, Lord. Take my life" (1 Kings 19:4, paraphrased). Let's examine some of Elijah's experiences that preceded his moment of hopelessness. (These events are recorded in 1 Kings 17 and 18.)

- Elijah informed King Ahab that there would be neither dew nor rain during the next few years.
- God directed Elijah to hide from Ahab in the Kerith Ravine. There, his water would be supplied by the brook and his food by ravens.
- When the brook dried up, God sent Elijah to Zarephath, where, again, he was fed miraculously—this time by a pauper widow who had a dependent son.
- Upon the death of the widow's son, Elijah prayed for the resurrection of the boy, and God brought the boy back to life.
- As the famine became severe because of the drought, Jezebel began to kill the Lord's prophets.
- Elijah participated in the ultimate test, which would determine whether Baal or Israel's God was the true God. The prophets of Baal asked their god to burn up their sacrificial bull, and Elijah called upon Jehovah to bring fire from heaven and burn the sacrifice he had laid on an altar. Only the Lord of heaven responded with blazing fire.
- Elijah had all the prophets of Baal slaughtered.
- He prayed for rain, and a heavy rain fell after three years of drought.

Notice that some of the above events weren't at all adverse. Some were positive events involving extraordinary manifestations of God's power.

Yet, all of them were stressful. Even emotional experiences of a positive nature can add to people's stress. The Holmes and Rahe Social Readjustment Rating Scale, a tool commonly used to quantify a person's stress, assigns forty-seven points to being fired from work, and fifty points to getting married.

We can imagine that all of the out-of-the-ordinary events that Elijah experienced filled his stress account till it was ready to burst. It was at that point that he encountered Jezebel's reaction to the slaughter of Baal's prophets. Her message was explicit: " 'May the gods deal with me, be it ever so severely, if by this time tomorrow I do not make your life like that of one of them [the prophets killed by sword]' " (1 Kings 19:2). This made Elijah run for his life all the way to Beersheba in Judah and to become desperate enough to say that he'd had enough and to ask the Lord to take his life.

Why didn't Elijah think of the miracles that had happened in the previous months? Why didn't he surrender to the same God who had given him power to resurrect a dead boy, brought fire from heaven, and sent profuse rain when Elijah prayed for it? Well, as human beings, this is our life story. By evening, we've forgotten a great blessing that came in the morning. But, wonderfully, God doesn't hold grudges. He picks up where we give up. He comes to our rescue and provides for our needs—just as He did for Elijah.

Heaven's way to manage stress

As soon as Elijah heard about Jezebel's intentions, he called his servant and fled with him to Beersheba—about ninety-five miles away. Then he left his servant there and went a day's journey into the desert by himself. Altogether, Elijah must have walked for an entire week at a steady, fast pace—after all, he was fleeing from death! Then he sat down by a broom tree, asked the Lord to take his life, and fell asleep.

In this emergency, God sent an angel to help the exhausted prophet. To end his thoughts of death and dying, he needed nourishment and sleep. Food excites most people, especially those with a good appetite, and Elijah must have had a fierce appetite after several days of hiking. No doubt the "cake" of bread cooked on coals and the jug of water must have been very restorative—after all, it was food prepared by an angel!

I'm not sure what would be the modern Middle Eastern equivalent to this bread, but in the Far East it would have to be something like a *bibingka*. Bibingkas are cakes of rice flour, coconut milk, and sugar, which are wrapped in banana leaves and baked on burning coals. When I lived in the Philippines and I wasn't traveling, I used to go to the market early every Sunday morning. I would always stop by the stand where bibingkas were sold and get some, which we would eat for breakfast with *salabat*—ginger tea. Bibingkas make me think of Elijah because they're big—five to six inches in diameter and as thick as a stack of two or three pancakes—enough for a hearty meal. And, like Elijah's bread, they're cooked on hot coals. After many years, I can still picture the radiant face of the plump, middle-aged woman who was surrounded by small piles of red coals, each of which had a bibingka baking on top of it. As soon as this woman saw me, she would give me a giant smile and ask, "One or two?"

Sometimes, fasting is good, but not when the spirit is abased. Food can supply not only nutrition but also the good mood so necessary for the stressed soul. And sleep follows in the angelic prescription. So Elijah took a siesta after his celestial meal.

I was born in and grew up in Spain. Perhaps the Spanish custom that shocks visitors the most is that of the lunchtime siesta. That meal, eaten at about two in the afternoon, tends to be the heaviest one of the day, and it's followed by a one- to two-hour-long nap—the siesta. Most working people live close to their job sites, which makes it easy for them to go home for lunch and siesta. And most jobs build their schedule around this practice: people work from 9 A.M. to 2 P.M. and 4 P.M. to 7 P.M. Sometimes, foreign tourists find it irritating because, with a few exceptions in the large cities, shops, museums, and other places of interest are closed for two hours (three in the summer) in the middle of the day. They don't know what to do with themselves during that time. But dividing the day into two distinct blocks separated by food, fellowship, and sleep breaks the stress of a full day's work.

The angel woke Elijah from his second nap and asked him to eat again as the journey was going to be a long one—he had to cover nearly two hundred miles to get to Mount Horeb (Mount Sinai). Ah, physical exercise works marvels for the stressed and strained! It's not used enough.

A few years ago, I bought a book by Robert E. Thayer, entitled *Calm Energy*,[4] thinking it was a self-help manual. Instead, the book is a collection of results of research done by the author and others on how people regulate mood with food and exercise. In the end, I was happy I bought it because I learned a number of practical mental health interventions as well as personal applications.

One of the studies assessed the subjective energy effects of 10 minutes of brisk walking as measured 30, 60, and 120 minutes after the exercise. Remarkably, ten minutes of exercise increases people's energy levels significantly for sixty minutes. Furthermore, results showed that those who exercised still had increased energy (weak but significant levels) even after two hours! The biggest finding of this and the other studies reported in the book is that physical exercise—even just twenty minutes of it—produces two changes in mood: first, feelings of energy, refreshment, and revival; and second, feelings of happiness, joy, and pleasure. I've had the chance to verify this myself on endless occasions.

After strenuous exercise, Elijah covered all the distance to Mount Sinai in "forty days and forty nights" (1 Kings 19:8). When he reached that mountain, he met with the Lord, heard His voice, and received the instructions for the tasks he would carry out before his departure to heaven. And though he continued to act as a prophet on these missions, we don't find him distressed anymore.

We know that after Elijah's intense life, his end was glorious. He was taken from earth to heaven in a whirlwind, escorted by a chariot of fire and horses of fire (see 2 Kings 2:11). We don't know what he's doing in heaven, but we know of one assignment carried out a few centuries after he got there: God sent Elijah and Moses, both experienced in human toil, from heaven to a mountain in Palestine to encourage Jesus before His passion and crucifixion.

Jesus' antistress strategies

Jesus, through His words and example, offered practical advice on how we can manage our daily stress. It was through His closeness to His Father and the support He received from others, such as His friends in Bethany, that He was able to face the heavy demands He experienced every day in healing, preaching, feeding multitudes, being tempted, and being persecuted by various groups of people. We can certainly extract lessons from what the Gospels tell us about Jesus.

Jesus bolstered His relationship with His Father through prayer and meditation. Mark tells us, for instance, that "very early in the morning, while it was still dark, Jesus got up, left the house and went off to a solitary place, where he prayed" (Mark 1:35). At times, Jesus invited His disciples to join Him. " 'Come with me by yourselves to a quiet place and get some rest,' " He said (Mark 6:31). Prayer in the quiet of the morning or evening may be the only time we can be impressed by the voice of God and receive the energy and wisdom to face the challenges life brings to us.

Jesus also found relief in fellowship. We find Him at times retiring to the house of Lazarus, Martha, and Mary. And He made sure that His disciples got some recreation. Ellen White noted that Jesus understood the needs His disciples had upon returning from a stressful mission. "Their labor had greatly elated and encouraged them, but it had also worn upon them," she wrote. Then Jesus led them to a desert place, which

> did not mean a waste and solitary wilderness, but a place of retirement and quiet, pleasant to the eyes and invigorating to the body. They sought such a place near a favorite resort on the Sea of Galilee. . . . The Christian life is not made up of unceasing activity or of continual meditation. . . . [Jesus] knew that a season of rest and recreation, apart from the multitude and the scene of [the disciples'] labors, would invigorate them, and He sought to withdraw them from the busy cities to a quiet resort where they might have a season of precious fellowship with Him and with each other. . . . The disciples of Jesus needed to be educated as to how they should labor and how they should rest. Today there is need that God's chosen workmen should listen to the command of Christ to go apart and rest awhile.[5]

We can also reduce stress through work—not just any kind of work, but labor to bring relief to others. Jesus' life was fundamentally selfless. He constantly used His energy to serve others. In a sermon, Peter summarized the life of Jesus as going " 'around doing good and healing all who were under the power of the devil' " (Acts 10:38).

People who engage in voluntary work, community projects, and so forth, report greater feelings of well-being and satisfaction than people who don't. Allan Luks and Peggy Payne studied 3,296 volunteers in the Big Brothers/Big Sisters program in New York City. Ninety-five percent of the volunteers reported a general sense of well-being and a growth in self-esteem. They also tended to perceive their negative experiences as minimal ones.[6]

If you are under a great deal of stress, you may need to put down those papers, tools, thoughts, or whatever and try to reflect on how Jesus dealt with overwork. And remember His promise: " 'Come to me, all you who are weary and burdened, and I will give you rest. Take my yoke upon you and learn from me, for I am gentle and humble in heart, and you will find rest for your souls' " (Matthew 11:28, 29).

1. Julian Kastrati, an Albanian and one of my students at Newbold College in England, and Ray Dabrowski, Trans-European Division communication director at the time, told me Flora Lewis's story.

2. Sheldon Cohen et al., "Psychological Stress and Susceptibility to the Common Cold," *New England Journal of Medicine* 42 (1991): 606–612.

3. Kevin Seybold, "Physiological Mechanisms Involved in Religiosity/Spirituality and Health," *Journal of Behavioral Medicine* 30 (2007): 303–309.

4. Robert E. Thayer, *Calm Energy: How People Regulate Mood With Food and Exercise* (Oxford: Oxford University Press, 2001), 35.

5. Ellen G. White, *My Life Today* (Washington, D.C.: Review and Herald® Publishing Association, 1952), 133.

6. See Allan Luks and Peggy Payne, *The Healing Power of Doing Good: The Health and Spiritual Benefits of Helping Others* (New York: Ballantine, 1992).

CHAPTER 4

Relationships

Pastor Carlos Rando, an evangelist from South America, held an evangelistic series in my church in Madrid, Spain, in the 1990s. His program consisted of a stress management seminar, followed by some lectures on the Bible and its message. Early in the series, he asked each person present to write on a piece of paper, in descending order, the top three sources of the stress they faced. Pastor Rando said he would use the survey results to introduce the following day's message.

As I helped with the collection and counting of the responses, I heard someone observe that Pastor Rando had already prepared transparencies that presented relationships as the number-one stressor for the audience. "But, Pastor Rando," the deacon objected, "we haven't finished counting yet!"

"Well," the evangelist said, "I've done this so many times and in so many places that I already know what the result will be—relationships, money, and health; or relationships, health, and money. Relationships are always first."

I find it very interesting that people tend to be the principal source of stress—and oftentimes, it's someone close to us: spouse, child, boss, neighbor, relative, friend, colleague, supplier, client, and so forth. Psychologists, counselors, and social workers know too well that when people come for help, they are likely to have problems with either self or others.

People can also bring much joy and satisfaction to our lives. When we achieve satisfying interactions with others, we experience happiness and

34

emotional development. But supportive and successful relationships don't happen without a reasonable investment of time, effort, and care. This includes kindness, humbleness, and the ability to receive and to give, to disclose and to endure, to confess and to forgive. The Bible offers endless counsel on maintaining optimal relationships. In this chapter I will discuss some of those passages and the principles they reveal that may help us in our relationships.

The rewards

The effects of positive relationships are overwhelming. John Robbins, the only son of the cofounder of the Baskin-Robbins ice-cream franchise, wrote a book titled *Healthy at 100*.[1] He obtained a large amount of data about groups of people known for their longevity, studying the inhabitants of Abkhazia, an autonomous region of Georgia on the western side of the Caucasus mountain range; the people of the Vilcabamba Valley, a remote area of Ecuador, situated high in the Andes near the border with Peru; the Hunzans, who live in a fertile valley surrounded by twenty-thousand-foot-high mountains in north Pakistan, near the border with China; and the citizens of the Japanese prefecture of Okinawa, who live in small villages scattered over the southernmost island of Japan. The people who live in these areas enjoy much greater levels of health and longevity than the rest of the world averages.

In spite of the difference in geographic location and culture, the diets and lifestyles of these people are remarkably similar. Furthermore, they all are privileged to have excellent social interactions. Family and community relationships are optimal, with constant exchange of kind, cordial, and loving messages. Life is free from competition. The people regard the elderly with a profound respect—almost reverence—for their maturity, wisdom, and contribution to the community. And delinquency is practically nonexistent.

Good relationships transmit the right kinds of moods, preventing depression, aiding in avoiding conflict and violence, and promoting togetherness. They also help us avoid intolerable stress. Social competence is a precious asset in human relations in general. This kind of skill allows us to gain a deep knowledge of people's feelings and motives, and enables fruitful work in groups and solutions through negotiation.

On the other hand, the mere absence of social interaction is problematic, and defective relationships bring much unhappiness and grief to everyone around. John Cacioppo, a professor at the University of Chicago, and his colleagues recruited subjects for a study of the association between loneliness and quality of sleep, the first study of its kind.[2] They selected individuals in the upper and lower 20 percent brackets of loneliness as measured by the UCLA-R Loneliness Scale. Then they studied their sleep patterns over a period of two weeks, having them each spend two nights in the research center with multiple sensors attached. The data analysis showed significant differences between the two groups. The participants who were lonely displayed poorer sleep efficiency, spending more time awake after sleep onset than did the participants who weren't lonely. In other studies, loneliness was seen as significantly reducing the probability of physical exercise in middle-aged people and as accelerating the rate of physiological deterioration in twenty-year-olds.[3]

But the quality of our relationships means much more than effectiveness and satisfaction. God has given us relationships so that we, His creatures, may give and receive love, care, concern, and empathy. That is why it is a topic of ongoing consideration in the Bible.

Humbleness and gentleness

The Bible contains an abundance of admonitions about the value of nourishing personal interactions. Six of the Ten Commandments have to do with maintaining right social interactions. The Bible also contains many stories that can teach us valuable lessons through their depiction of how people interact.

Paul considered teaching the members of the early church how to preserve the Christlike spirit that should characterize Christ's followers to be one of the primary tasks of his ministry. That's why his letters contain counsel for husbands and wives, parents and children, employers and employees, free men and slaves, church leaders and parishioners, government leaders and citizens. Paul insisted on Jesus' love message to the early church: "Let no debt remain outstanding, except the continuing debt to love one another, for he who loves his fellowman has fulfilled the law" (Romans 13:8; cf. Galatians 5:14). And on numerous occasions, he promoted love, service, compassion, kindness, humility, gentleness, patience, forgiveness, hospitality, truthfulness, fairness, peacefulness, submission, readiness to encourage, openness to being counseled, respect, tolerance, and peacemaking. All of these qualities have to do with establishing, maintaining, and enhancing interpersonal connections.

Paul wrote several times on the themes of humbleness and submissiveness: "Be completely humble and gentle" (Ephesians 4:2). "Submit to one another" (Ephesians 5:21). He regarded these themes as important because one of the strongest barriers to positive human interactions is the universal struggle for power. It was present in his day, and it's a part of our lives now. It touches families, friendships, workplaces, and churches. Any cooperative project runs the risk of power struggles—one or more parties may attempt to gain control over the others in order to satisfy their own needs. Interestingly, many of those in need of power act as they do because of their low self-esteem. Abusers, for example, have less self-esteem than most other people. Our self-esteem increases when we realize how much God values us (see chapter 9).

Social psychologists who study how people relate to each other have noted an interesting fact: when two people talk to each other or when someone does something in the presence of another person, they tend to display either a top-down or a bottom-up attitude. This is evidenced through the kinds of words they use and the nonverbal cues they display. If two people show a top-down demeanor in their encounter with each other, the interaction may become violent or at least unproductive. If one adopts a bottom-up and the other a top-down attitude, the interaction may be balanced but at risk of discomfort because of the unequal roles. But when the interaction is truly bottom-up on both sides, the parties involved attempt to build each other up, to empower each other. This kind of interaction is close to what Paul called for when he encouraged Christians to submit to one another. The result is likely to be a smooth relationship, with a full sharing of power and responsibilities.

Abigail's story

First Samuel 25 tells the story of a woman, Abigail, who was able to save dozens of lives through her remarkable social competence. Abigail was married to a man named *Nabal*, which means "fool." Nabal was very rich, but he was also mean and socially illiterate—he had no tact and no understanding of the realities of life. Various English translations use the following appellatives to describe him: *churlish, harsh, brutish, rough, crude,* as well as *evil, mean,* and *badly behaved.* Nabal's nature must have provided much fodder for conversation in his household. I can imagine one of his servants saying, "He's such a wicked man that no one can talk to him."

David, who had defended Nabal's interests at no cost to him, sent emissaries to Nabal to request—very kindly and respectfully—food for his soldiers. But Nabal refused to give the soldiers anything, and he treated them with disrespect. As soon as Abigail heard about her husband's preposterous behavior, she devised an emergency plan. Note some of the steps she took.

- Her immediate action: she arranged for the servants to give David's men about a ton of food, the commodity they needed most.
- Her nonverbal messages: when she saw David, she quickly got off her donkey and bowed down before him with her face to the ground.
- Her speech: she expressed her good wishes with language that exalted God and called for His blessings upon David and his descendants.
- Her acknowledgment of Nabal's folly: in her report to David she called her own husband "wicked" and "fool."
- Her respectful language: Abigail constantly referred to David as "my master" and to herself as "your servant."
- Her appeal: she begged for forgiveness on behalf of her husband and invited David not to burden his conscience with the blood of many innocent people.

David granted Abigail's petition, and Nabal died of shock when he heard what had been about to happen to him and his household. This is how Abigail prevented a great number of casualties. Soon after this, David took Abigail as his wife.

Repay evil with blessings

Nabal was asked to repay good done for him with blessings, and he failed to do what seems natural and reasonable. Jesus taught His followers to take an additional step—to repay *evil* with blessings! Unassisted human beings can't do this, but a gift from the Spirit that offers a glimpse of God's character makes it possible.

John Selwyn (1844–1898), who became bishop of the Melanesian Mission in the South Pacific at the age of thirty, had been known for his boxing skill in his college days at Eton and Cambridge. One day he had to chide an islander who had a temper. Unhappy with what Selwyn said, the islander clenched his fist and struck Selwyn in the face. The bishop, who still was very strong, could have knocked the islander down, but he didn't retaliate. Instead, he kept looking at his attacker's face with serenity. The aggressor was so ashamed of himself that he ran away into the jungle.

The incident passed without much notice; but years later, when Selwyn had returned to England, the man who had struck him came to the bishop who had taken Selwyn's place to confess his faith and be baptized. When he was asked what new name he wished to have, he responded, "*John Selwyn,* for he taught me what Jesus is like."

We can learn more of this principle of repaying evil or insult with blessings from how David related to King Saul, who repeatedly tried to kill him. On one occasion, Saul went into a cave to relieve himself—the very cave in which David and his men were hiding. David's men wanted to kill Saul, but David prevented them from harming him. Moments later, Saul and David had a healing encounter just outside the cave. David explained his motives to Saul, and Saul wept as he recognized his mistake.

Unfortunately, this reconciliation didn't last long. Soon Saul and three thousand of his men were searching for David again. One night, David and one of his leaders, Abishai, infiltrated Saul's sleeping army and made it all the way to Saul's bedside. They could have killed him then and there, but David told Abishai, " 'Don't destroy him! . . . The LORD himself will strike him; either his time will come and he will die, or he will go into battle and perish. But the LORD forbid that I should lay a hand on the LORD's anointed' " (1 Samuel 26:9–11).

What a beautiful attitude David had toward the man who was trying to kill him! How different would be the quality of our relationships if we would let God take whatever revenge might be needed, and in the meantime, just like David, we would continue our attempts to make peace.

Forgiveness

Forgiveness is another aspect of God's nature, which He will supply to His children so they can build better relationships. Forgiveness is among the "techniques" currently recommended in spiritual and religious counseling—together with prayer, reading of sacred passages, singing, worshiping, journaling, and so forth. Psychology hasn't always included forgiveness as a support for healing. However, nonreligious as well as religious counselors now consider it to be a legitimate tool. The professional literature often contains argumentation for forgiveness.

Forgiveness enhances positive feelings, helps people put aside issues and troubles, favors the restoration of lost relationships, and helps unload a heavy psychological burden of hostility. (However, secular psychologists carefully avoid the term *sin* because secular psychology still excludes that term!) Now, forgiveness is considered to be a valid option when a spouse is abandoned for another partner, an employee is wrongfully dismissed, one's reputation is ruined through gossip, or someone is victim of a financial scam. It makes sense. People realize that holding grudges and fighting back is quite expensive in terms of mental health and well-being and usually doesn't solve anything or provide any other benefit than the dubious one of getting even.

But there is something even greater than preserving mental health. Scripture encourages us to practice forgiveness because it makes us more like Jesus. "Be kind and compassionate to one another, forgiving each other, just as in Christ God forgave you" (Ephesians 4:32).

A true and beautiful story of forgiveness is that of Jo Berry. Her father, Sir Anthony Berry, a member of the British parliament, was killed by an IRA bomb in 1984, together with four other people. The man responsible for the attack was Patrick Magee, who served fourteen years in jail before being released in 1999 under the terms of the 1998 Good Friday agreement.

Jo met Patrick in 2000. They talked for three hours, and then Patrick said, "I have never met anyone like you before. I don't know what to say. I want to hear your pain." They had other opportunities to meet and deepen their friendship. Patrick expressed remorse for the innocent lives that were lost as a result of his violence, and Jo came to understand much better the life Patrick had led and how he ended up doing what he did. Their friendship has not only been healing to both of them, but they have become agents of action for peace. They have spoken to young people in Austria, Israel, South Africa, and Spain about peace and forgiveness. In October 2009, they gave their testimony at the British parliament as part of a program on forgiveness.

The last moments in Jesus' life show us the supreme example of His forgiveness. Jesus prayed, " 'Father, forgive them, for they do not know what they are doing' " (Luke 23:34). Ellen White wrote, "All heaven was filled with wonder when the prayer of Christ was offered in the midst of His terrible suffering."[4]

Sometimes one may think that forgiveness is virtually impossible to grant, and indeed that is the case, for there is too much selfishness in the human heart. But forgiving people even heinous wrongs they have committed against us is possible when the Holy Spirit removes our hearts of stone and gives us hearts of flesh (see Ezekiel 36:26).

Relationships

Confession and support at church

I grew up as a Catholic and attended Catholic schools, so confession was part of my growing years. It would have been much simpler to confess to God than to follow the doctrine of the confessional, which was based on a twisted interpretation of James 5:16, "Therefore confess your sins to each other." But at that time, the confessional was all that I knew. So, once a week, we boys were taken to the chapel to confess. It was a bit awkward the first few times, but one gets used to it.

Then a rumor started that the priest told the principal whatever sins we confessed. When the principal heard about the rumor, he was shocked and decided that he would bring in two more priests on confession day to guarantee the secrecy of the confessional. At first, many of the pupils went to the new priests, but that choice soon became unpopular, for those priests assigned time-consuming penances. Within a few weeks, our own in-house priest had all the boys back again because he systematically assigned just five Hail Marys (which literally took only forty-five seconds to chant) as penance for any sin we committed.

My understanding of James 5:16 is much more meaningful now. This verse tells me that if I offend my neighbor, I am required to confess to him or her in order to secure forgiveness and restore the relationship. Disclosing my trespasses to my neighbor brings maturity to our relationship. One of the greatest needs human beings have is to talk with someone who cares. The caring listener has the tremendous privilege of empathizing and providing support. The exchange of confession and forgiveness relieves emotional burdens and establishes a deeper level of mutual commitment that makes the relationship safer and more profound and lasting.

However, we must remember that not everyone lives by the ethics of confidentiality. Unfortunately, it isn't unusual for people to share confided secrets with their friends and fellow church members. This can produce a great deal of pain. Thus, we need to trust only those people who have demonstrated unquestionable discretion. In any case, fervent prayer can bring relief to the soul with zero risk of breaching the bond of confidentiality.

Let's look again at the golden rule: " 'In everything, do to others what you would have them do to you' " (Matthew 7:12). This principle is a priceless jewel for social relationships. It is positive, universal, based on love, and stretches above and beyond human law. It guarantees optimal interactions. However, we need divine help to put this divine principle into practice.

Mental and Emotional Health

The story is told of two American Indians who were sitting by a fire on a placid evening, Chief Teedyuscung of the Delawares and an unnamed close friend of his. For some time, they sat together without saying much, each of them reflecting on his own concerns. The friend was thinking of interpersonal problems and remembered he had once heard of the Christian golden rule. He turned to Teedyuscung and said, "Chief, once I heard a principle of excellence and great usefulness."

Teedyuscung raised his open hand to stop his friend from continuing. Then he said, "Do not tell me of the excellence or praises of that principle. Just say it to me, and I will tell you if it is trustworthy."

So, in plain and brief terms, his friend explained the golden rule to Teedyuscung. The chief immediately exclaimed, "That's impossible!" Then the two men sat in quietness for several minutes.

Eventually, Teedyuscung broke the silence. He said, "I have thought of that golden rule, and I say that if the Great Spirit that created man would give him a new heart, then it would be possible!"

If you don't know what to do about an issue you have with someone, run your question through the simple test of the golden rule: If I were in his/her place, what would I prefer to be done? What would I not like to be done? Then ask God for strength, wisdom, and guidance on what to do.

---

1. John Robbins, *Healthy at 100: The Scientifically Proven Secrets of the World's Healthiest and Longest-Lived Peoples* (New York: Random House, 2006).

2. John T. Cacioppo et al., "Do Lonely Days Invade the Nights?" *Psychological Science* 13 (2002): 384–387.

3. Louise C. Hawkley et al., "Loneliness Predicts Reduced Physical Activity: Cross-Sectional and Longitudinal Analyses," *Health Psychology* 28 (2009): 354–363; Louise C. Hawkley and John T. Cacioppo, "Aging and Loneliness," *Current Directions in Psychological Science* 16 (2007): 187–191.

4. Ellen G. White, *The Desire of Ages,* 760.

CHAPTER 5

Guilt

In his book *How to Stop Feeling Guilty,* Dr. Vernon Coleman tells the story of a young man who spent the evening partying at a pub and drank more than he should have.[1] When he drove his car home that night, he wasn't very alert. As he turned a corner, he felt that he had hit something. But he ignored whatever it was, drove on home, and went to bed.

The next day, when his mind was clearer, he remembered the thud he'd felt the night before. He looked at the front of his car and saw that it was dented, and then he calculated where on his route home it was likely that he'd had the collision. Later that day, he read in the newspaper that on the previous night, in the place where he surmised he'd felt the bump, a vehicle had struck an old woman, killing her, and then had left the scene of the accident. The young man concluded that he had killed the woman, but, fearing the consequences, he chose to remain silent.

From that time on, guilt plagued the man. He rehearsed the scene many a time and felt miserable about it—eventually, even having auditory hallucinations. He often considered making a confession, but he never did. Some twenty years after the event, he decided that he couldn't stand the guilt he felt any longer and committed suicide. He left a note, in which he explained that he was the irresponsible driver who had killed the woman found that night twenty years earlier.

The police investigating the case consulted the newspaper story of the woman's death. They found that the reporter who wrote the newspaper story had made a mistake. The old lady had been killed at the same place

43

where the man had felt the bump, but she had died on the night before he had his accident—so, obviously, somebody else had hit her!

Guilt is the remorseful awareness of having done something morally wrong. Feeling guilty is one of the most uncomfortable experiences people endure. In addition to being highly unpleasant and at times incapacitating, it may cause shame, sorrow, anger, anxiety, distress, and even organic illness. There are several levels of guilt, from guilt based on a true violation of a universal principle to the neurotic guilt that, though totally unfounded, dominates someone's mind and makes life miserable with no redeeming purpose.

Transgression of the moral law brings a sense of guilt. This is a good thing. It is the mechanism God put into place to make His creatures aware that sin always brings pain to oneself and to others. This is the guilt that a father may experience after losing his temper and verbally abusing his wife and children. Moments later, he may feel awful, with no appetite, be unable to sleep, and have muscular pains and self-hatred. Although some people resist this emotion until they become used to it, others feel compelled to repent, ask the wronged persons and God for forgiveness, and do what they can to diminish the chances of it happening again. This is real redemptive guilt, and it often brings good results. We'll look at several Bible stories in which guilt was the main motive behind people's behavior.

The ultimatum game

Even a little bit of guilt may prove useful, as shown in a study conducted by Timothy Ketelaar from the University of California, Los Angeles and Wing Tung Au from the Chinese University of Hong Kong.[2] They selected seventy-two undergraduate students, grouped them in pairs, and asked them to play the ultimatum game. The researchers told each pair they could share nineteen dollars. Partner one was to make an offer on how to share the money—a single offer in a sealed envelope. Partner two couldn't alter the offer or pose a counteroffer; he or she had to simply accept it or reject it. If partner two accepted the offer, the money was divided between the two of them. If not, the researchers kept the money.

Characteristically, partner twos tended to reject very low offers. In other words, rather than accept an offer that would bring them a little money—and the partner ones considerably more—they preferred to reject the money altogether to punish the greedy partner ones who wanted the lion's share of the money.

Sometimes when a partner two accepted a low offer, the partner one experienced guilt. Ketelaar and Au found this when they administered a guilt scale to the thirty-six partner ones in their study. The researchers repeated the game one week later, and they found that those who felt guilty in the first game raised their offer considerably in the second game even though their partners were likely to accept their low offers. Their guilt moved them toward fairness.

When we feel guilty about inconsequential or nonexistent matters, guilt can be a nuisance or even a psychological burden. The people who are overly sensitive to guilt are those who experience it for irrelevant things. These people score high on a personality trait called *guilt-proneness*. In these cases, guilt becomes a barrier rather than a means of improvement. One example would be a woman who is bothered by guilt for several hours because she ate a cookie when she hadn't intended to eat any. Or a man who feels guilty because, due to the pressure of time, he passed one of his neighbors without stopping and chatting for a few minutes. Guilt-prone individuals can be manipulated easily. Children know this well; they soon discover which parent will yield to a request when it is accompanied with a pout.

There are still more pathological forms of guilt in which the mechanism malfunctions and makes people feel guilty about something for which they aren't responsible. This is called *neurotic guilt*. It doesn't necessarily go away with time but often needs the intervention of a mental health professional. Examples of this kind of guilt include survivors of a calamity who feel guilty because their friends or family lost their lives and nothing happened to them. The family of someone who committed suicide may feel responsible for the loss. Children whose parents divorce may experience guilt feelings because they think they caused the split. These forms of guilt cause much psychological pain and emotional turmoil with no apparent purpose.

Let's examine four biblical accounts in which people experienced guilt—the stories of Adam and Eve, Joseph's brothers, David, and Peter. A look at their lives can teach us how to make good use of this emotion.

Adam and Eve

Genesis 3 says that immediately after Adam and Eve disobeyed, they experienced a cluster of emotions, including guilt, worry, and dread. This brought about significant changes in their behavior—they suddenly realized they were naked and hid from the Lord as soon as they heard Him coming. Then the following interesting dialogue took place:

GOD. What is this you have done?

ADAM. The woman you put here with me—she gave me some fruit from the tree, and I ate it.

EVE. The serpent deceived me, and I ate.

Sigmund Freud, the founder of psychoanalysis, would have called this the first occurrence of projection—a defense mechanism in which people blame someone else for the mistake they themselves have made. According to Freud, people use projection to defend themselves from excessive guilt and anxiety. That's true, but burdening an innocent person with the responsibility for our actions is immoral.

A story is told of a Chinese prime minister whose handwriting wasn't very legible. Once he had a beautiful thought that he wanted to commit to writing. He grabbed a brush and wrote his maxim on paper so that it would be immortalized. Then he called his nephew to copy it in beautiful characters, for his nephew was an excellent calligrapher. The young man started to write down the sentence, but coming to a difficult-to-decipher character, took the paper to his uncle for clarification. The prime minister studied the character carefully but couldn't decipher his own handwriting. Then, staring at his nephew, he said, "Why didn't you ask me before, when the sentence was fresh in my mind?"

In this world's first instance of someone blaming someone else, Adam tried to unload his guilt on Eve. She didn't want to take responsibility either, so she tried to unload it onto the serpent. But blaming others doesn't solve the problem and may seriously affect interpersonal relationships. Besides, it poses a barrier to God's forgiveness. It's better to accept full responsibility for one's own action and seek the only One who can provide freedom from guilt: "There is now no condemnation for those who are in Christ Jesus" (Romans 8:1).

Joseph's brothers

When Jacob sent his sons to purchase grain in Egypt, they were reminded of their sale of their brother to slave traders. They talked about it while standing near Joseph, apparently thinking that this "Egyptian ruler" didn't understand their language. Their conversation reveals that they were still carrying around a load of guilt, and it's likely that their evil deed had been a recurring topic of conversation over the years. On this occasion they were saying to each other, " 'Surely we are being punished because of our brother. We saw how distressed he was when he pleaded with us for his life, but we would not listen; that's why this distress has come upon us' " (Genesis 42:21). To which Reuben, the oldest brother, said, " 'Didn't I tell you not to sin against the boy? But you wouldn't listen! Now we must give an accounting for his blood' " (verse 22).

People with intense guilt who do nothing about it may experience the guilt-producing event repeatedly. It can recur in the form of intrusive thoughts or flashback images that flood one's mind, or it may appear in dreams or nightmares. It's reasonable to think that the image of young Joseph, upset and imploring for mercy, had been replayed numerous times in his brothers' minds. Joseph knew better than anyone else the root of his brothers' emotional trouble. So, with a noble attitude, he invited them, " 'Come close to me. . . . I am your brother Joseph, the one you sold into Egypt! And now, do not be distressed and do not be angry with yourselves for selling me here, because it was to save lives that God sent me ahead of you' " (Genesis 45:4, 5).

God made provision to free these men from the burden of guilt. After more than twenty years of remorse, the right time and conditions liberated them from their bondage. Joseph forgave them, and with no conditions attached, he urged them not to be angry at themselves any longer.

Guilt can be quite helpful in smaller things as well. A study conducted at the University of Helsinki, Finland, showed that reparative and conciliatory behaviors were more often reported when the subjects were experiencing guilt than when they were experiencing shame.[3] Researcher Silfver selected ninety-seven university students and asked each to provide one to three narratives based on the following questions: (a) What was the situation in which you felt guilt, shame, or both? What did you think, feel, and do in the situation? (b) What kind of thoughts or behavior did you use to alleviate the guilt or shame? (c) Were you successful in alleviating these emotions or did you continue to suffer from guilt or shame? When the data was content analyzed and the responses were classified by their emotional meaning, the following results emerged.

- The majority of accounts (62 percent) described interpersonal situations as the source of guilt or shame. For example, the subject hadn't been a good friend, parent, spouse, or relative. Others felt guilty for not having helped someone in need (e.g., a drunk or the poor).
- Fourteen percent of the answers showed guilt or shame for violating personal and/or societal norms, such as by cheating on a

test, shoplifting, or having illicit sex.

- Thirteen percent of the narratives reported guilt or shame associated with individual duties—for example, feeling guilty or ashamed for not keeping the house clean and tidy, not spending enough time working or studying, overeating, and so forth.
- Eleven percent of the accounts involved guilt or shame connected with being a victim: having been molested, harassed, or abused.

Guilt was found to motivate the subjects to initiate and follow through on reparative behaviors—to avoid the behavior that had produced the guilt, to reconcile, and so forth. The researchers also found that those who were victims were more likely to have experienced repetitive rumination than were the ones who had violated standards. This makes sense because victims don't have to make reparations, and their guilt is generally unfounded. These cases tend to require professional intervention.

David's sapped strength

David is most creative in expressing the consequences of guilt as well as in showing the way to escape it.

When I kept silent,
  my bones wasted away
  through my groaning all day long. . . .
My strength was sapped
  as in the heat of summer (Psalm 32:3, 4).

In referring to the results of guilt, Psalm 38 uses expressions like *overwhelming, a burden too heavy to bear, loathsome, mourning all day long, searing pain in the back, feebleness, utterly crush, anguish of heart, pounding heart, vision problems,* and *social rejection.* The language depicts not only the anguish that sin produces, but also the physical weakness and pain that it brings. Guilt affects the body as well as the soul—states of mind produced by emotional turmoil, such as continuous guilt, may cause a variety of psychosomatic reactions.

A team of researchers led by Nicholas Hall made important breakthroughs in the field of psycho-neuroimmunology. They found intimate mind-body connections in the following illnesses: AIDS, breast cancer, chronic fatigue syndrome, the common cold, melanoma, multiple sclerosis, and tuberculosis.[4] Psychotherapists know that providing clients with an opportunity to express their feelings to an empathic listener puts them on the path to healing. In Psalm 32, David says his Lord is the most understanding Person—and One who also has the power to grant complete forgiveness. He says that relief comes as soon as confession takes place:

> Then I acknowledged my sin to you
>   and did not cover up my iniquity.
> I said, "I will confess
>   my transgressions to the Lord"—
> and you forgave
>   the guilt of my sin (Psalm 32:5).

A historic example of the burden guilt produces is the experience of Charles IX, king of France, who ordered the massacre of the Huguenots (French Protestants) on St. Bartholomew's Day, August 24, 1572. Several thousand Protestants—men, women, and children—were killed in Paris and the provinces. Afterwards, the king complained to his physician, "I don't know what ails me, my whole frame seems in a fever. I see nothing around me but hideous faces covered with blood. At night I awake to a concert of screams, groaning, howling, and furious voices, menacing and blaspheming just as they were heard on the night of the massacre."[5]

Peter's bitter weeping

God emphatically disapproves of His children making a formal statement of commitment or a gift and then reneging on their word. Peter's impulsiveness led him to affirm his faithfulness to the Lord at all costs. First, he contrasted himself with the other disciples: " 'Even if all fall away on account of you, I never will' " (Matthew 26:33). Then he contradicted Jesus, who had told him that he would disown Him three times. No, Peter declared, " 'Even if I have to die with you, I will never disown you' " (verse 35). But hours later he did deny Jesus—and he did so not because he was being coerced by powerful soldiers or people in authority, but because two girls and a servant of the high priest asked him whether he was one of Jesus' disciples. He repeatedly said that he didn't know Jesus, and eventually *swore to them,* " 'I don't know the man!' " The rooster crowed right after Peter spoke those words, and he was instantly reminded of the Master's statement that he would disown Him three times. And when Peter recognized what he had done, he wept bitterly.

In the 1870s, Ellen G. White counseled a man who had been involved in spiritualism and was going through a severe trial. She explained to him that that he needed to suffer for a while so he could serve others adequately. She commented that in denying the Savior, Peter went through a very bitter experience, but those painful moments were crucial for his transformation and preparation for his future ministry. She wrote,

> He [Peter] afterward repented and was reconverted. He had true contrition of soul and gave himself afresh to his Savior. With blinding tears he makes his way to the solitudes of the Garden of Gethsemane and there prostrates himself where he saw his Savior's prostrate form when the bloody sweat was forced from His pores by His great agony. Peter remembers with remorse that he was asleep when Jesus prayed during those fearful hours. His proud heart breaks, and penitential tears moisten the sods so recently stained with the bloody sweat drops of God's dear Son. He left that garden a converted man.[6]

The first half of the book of Acts provides clear evidence of Peter's transformation. His preaching, leadership, and healing were extraordinary, leading to the salvation of many people and the foundation of the church as the body of Christ. He counted his death, anticipated by Jesus (see John 21:18), an honor, for he died in the same manner as his Master.

Solving the problem of guilt

Paul expressed his struggle with sin and the law in multiple ways in Romans 7. Then, in the very next chapter, he made a categorical statement that offers great hope for humanity: "Therefore, there is now no condemnation for those who are in Christ Jesus" (Romans 8:1).

The solution to guilt arising from either an offense to God or to a fellow human being can come only from Jesus. His grace allows us to repent and go to our brother or sister for reconciliation (James 5:16). His sacrifice also entitles us to God's forgiveness (1 John 1:9). With the exceptions of the pathological guilt mentioned above, any person under the burden of guilt must repent and confess his wrong to the offended neighbor to obtain forgiveness. This is to be done before the sinner makes any attempt to reconcile with God (Matthew 5:23, 24). Then, the person must confess to God. As a result, full pardon takes place.

If guilt is weighing you down in any way, examine the origin of the trouble and see if any other person is involved. If so, take responsibility and repent, make a concerted effort to obtain forgiveness and reconciliation, and then go directly to God to obtain the forgiveness He promises. Remember, He wants to forgive. He takes no pleasure in the death of anyone; He wants you to " 'repent and live' " (Ezekiel 18:32).

1. Vernon Coleman, *How to Stop Feeling Guilty* (London: Sheldon Press, 1987).

2. Timothy Ketelaar and Wing Tung Au, "The Effects of Feelings of Guilt on the Behaviour of Uncooperative Individuals in Repeated Social Bargaining Games: An Effect-as-Information Interpretation of the Role of Emotion in Social Interaction," *Cognition and Emotion* 17 (2003): 429–453.

3. Mia Silfver, "Coping With Guilt and Shame: A Narrative Approach," *Journal of Moral Education* 36 (2007): 169–183.

4. Nicholas Hall et al., eds., *Mind-Body Interactions and Disease and Psychoneuro-immunological Aspects of Health and Disease: Proceedings of a Conference on Stress, Immunity and Health Sponsored by the National Institutes of Health* (Celebration, Fla.: Health Dateline Press, 1996).

5. Paul Lee Tan, *Encyclopedia of 15,000 Illustrations* (Dallas Bible Communications, 1998), CD-ROM, entry 1773.

6. Ellen G. White, *Testimonies for the Church* (Mountain View, Calif.: Pacific Press®, 1948), 3:416.

CHAPTER 6

Thinking

At the age of thirty, Joel* was a successful professional with a rewarding and stable position at a software firm. He was also an active Christian who helped his church in various capacities, especially with his computer expertise. He had maintained a good friendship with a young woman from the church that could have ended in marriage, but she decided that he wasn't her type and walked out of the relationship. This left Joel very troubled and insecure—to the point that he wasn't willing to attempt another courtship.

Joel's problem was compounded by lust. He had acquired the habit of fantasizing sexually about women he saw at work or elsewhere. After he held an ordinary conversation with a woman he liked, he would almost always follow up by imagining sexual encounters, and sometimes he ended up masturbating.

Joel felt very uncomfortable with all this. As a Christian, he felt that what he was experiencing wasn't God's plan for relationships and sexuality, and he didn't like that. He prayed about his problem from time to time, but it didn't go away. He thought of seeking counseling but decided that his issue was too embarrassing to talk about. Finally, however, he decided to talk to his college roommate, who had completed a graduate degree in counseling. He didn't want formal counseling; he just wanted to share his burden with someone discreet and perhaps get some tips on how to solve his problem.

---

*A pseudonym.

Thinking

Although at first Joel found it difficult to talk about his concerns, eventually he told his friend everything. They had a two-hour conversation in which Joel did most of the talking and explained all the details of his problem. He was also surprised that his former roommate didn't look at him strangely or judge his deviant behavior, but instead showed willingness to help him as a dear friend. The conversation gave Joel a great sense of relief.

The two men met five or six times over the course of two months, and Joel was delighted with the results. He was also excited about the approach his friend had followed, which included drawing the power of the Holy Spirit into the process. For him, one of the drawbacks of secular counseling was that the therapist would likely try to convince him that there was no reason to feel guilty about this behavior because it supposedly didn't hurt anyone. His friend, being a man of faith, had included spirituality in the psychotherapy, and they always prayed during their meetings.

What did Joel learn in the sessions with his former roommate? He learned that the patterns of thought he harbored before, during, and after his behaviors, were of utmost importance. He also came to understand how the more frequently he went through these patterns, the more deeply rooted his habit became. He, therefore, had to be continually aware of his thoughts, feelings, and emotions.

One of Joel's homework assignments was to keep a record of the most significant feelings and emotions he experienced each day, as well as the events and thoughts surrounding them. Then, together, he and his therapist friend tried to find the meaning of his emotions and thoughts and their connection with the problem. Joel learned that in order to stop thinking lustful thoughts, he had to identify the stimuli—circumstances, persons, thoughts, and so forth—that initiated them. Then he could avoid or reject those stimuli.

Underlying issues

Joel also learned about his underlying issues. The lustful thoughts and masturbation were surface manifestations of deeper problems. For example, he had difficulty dealing with female friends in a natural and relaxed way. He also realized that he had personal insecurities that prevented him from relating to all people naturally. The core issue was that he was very afraid to be rejected by women, possibly because of the rejection by his girlfriend. He also thought he bored people and kept repeating to himself,

"How boring I am." All these issues required attention and action, so he learned some strategies that his friend called "self-instruction." He had to drop the negativistic and unrealistic thoughts and beliefs about himself and replace them with others that he and his friend agreed were satisfactory. His therapist friend also gave him the homework assignment of holding positive conversations with female friends in a natural manner without following them up with sexual fantasies. He even rehearsed some of these encounters with his friend to gain confidence and skill.

Lastly, he learned something for which he would be forever grateful. He learned to depend on God via consistent, frequent prayer. Joel had a watch that beeped on the hour. At the beep, he would pause and offer a short prayer thanking God for specific blessings, great and small, and for strength to win the battle. The hourly beeping of his watch caught him in many different places and situations, but he always prayed. He started to pray for others too—for his family, friends, coworkers, for those women he had lusted for, and even for the strangers in his life. Although initially this was a counseling assignment, he kept this practice even after the treatment.

Many of the routines Joel followed are part of a widely used form of psychotherapy known as "cognitive-behavioral therapy" (CBT). The basic theory behind CBT techniques is that people are emotionally disturbed not just by events and circumstances, but by how they process their thoughts. The approach has two basic components: thinking (cognitive) and acting (behavioral). Joel needed to change both his thinking and his behavior. The point is that once he changed his thinking, he found it rather natural to change what he did.

Those who practice CBT believe that a positive and reasonable outlook can produce both a better mood and better results in all sorts of areas: personal, interpersonal, and more. They also believe that if people's thinking is exaggerated, hopeless, unhelpful, biased, and distorted, they are likely to become dysfunctional. That is, people who apply faulty thoughts to themselves, to others, to current events, the past, and the future will become angry, upset, worried, hostile, and depressed.

The thinking-acting connection and the possibility of personal control apply to multiple situations: work, family, friendships, stressful events, etc., all very important areas of mental health. In addition, our spiritual life is notably affected by the way we think. The Bible teaches us about the connection between thoughts and actions, both good and evil. It also reminds us of our responsibility to control our thoughts and submit them to the obedience of Christ (2 Corinthians 10:5). In the rest of this chapter we'll extract some lessons from scriptural admonitions and stories that will make us more aware of the importance of our thinking and will help us find divine support to make necessary changes.

As a person thinks . . .

Reflecting Christ, a devotional book compiled from Ellen G. White's writings (published in 1985), includes a piece titled "What You Think, You Are."[1] It's a commentary on 2 Corinthians 10:5 that originally was printed in the *Signs of the Times*° on August 23, 1905, and it includes some powerful statements on how crucial our thinking is to the battle of the soul. Here are some of those statements:

- More precious than the golden wedge of Ophir is the power of right thought. We need to place a high value upon the right control of our thoughts; for such control prepares us to labor for the Master. It is necessary for our peace and happiness in this life that our thoughts center in Christ. As a man thinketh, so is he.
- Every impure thought defiles the soul, impairs the moral sense, and tends to obliterate the impressions of the Holy Spirit. It dims the spiritual vision, so that men cannot behold God.
- The converting power of God changes the heart, refining and purifying the thoughts. Unless a determined effort is made to keep the thoughts centered on Christ, grace cannot reveal itself in the life. The mind must engage in the spiritual warfare.
- We need a constant sense of the ennobling power of pure thoughts and the damaging influence of evil thoughts. Let us place our thoughts upon holy things. Let them be pure and true; for the only security for any soul is right thinking. We are to use every means that God has placed within our reach for the government and cultivation of our thoughts. We are to bring our minds into harmony with Christ's mind. His truth will sanctify us, body, soul, and spirit, and we shall be enabled to rise above temptation.

Thought determines behavior; both good and bad deeds come from the heart (mind) rather than from outside.

Mark 7 tells a story in which Jesus emphasizes the mind-first, action-second sequence. Jesus noticed that the Pharisees and some teachers of the law were very concerned about the ceremonial washing of the hands. They were criticizing the disciples because they often forgot to do this washing and consequently were eating their food with ceremonially unclean hands. Jesus confronted them with a valid perspective. He rebuked them for sometimes breaking the Ten Commandments while holding to the tradition of the elders. For example, to keep their money and property for themselves, these religious leaders declared it to be "Corban." This was a "legal" way to make the leaders technically unable to share their wealth with their parents, no matter how needy they might be. Really, however, they were breaking the fifth commandment.

Jesus repeatedly explained that nothing that entered people from the outside—because of, for instance, a failure to do the ceremonial washings of their hands—makes them morally unclean. Rather, He said, " 'From within, out of men's hearts, come evil thoughts, sexual immorality, theft, murder, adultery, greed, malice, deceit, lewdness, envy, slander, arrogance and folly. All these evils come from inside and make a man "unclean" ' " (Mark 7:21–23). By this Jesus revealed that all of us will be held accountable for the actions that come from within us—and that we can't simply blame the environment, circumstances, or past experiences.

On a different occasion, Jesus reinforced the same idea using the tree-fruit connection as an illustration. " 'People,' " He said, " 'do not pick figs from thornbushes, or grapes from briers. The good man brings good things out of the good stored up in his heart [mind], and the evil man brings evil things out of the evil stored up in his heart. For out of the overflow of his heart his mouth speaks' " (Luke 6:44, 45).

While counseling a couple in the Far East, I had the opportunity to share with them some of my strategies as well as to learn from them. The husband had an anger control problem. Small stimuli would make him raise his voice like a mad man, and, on occasion, he even physically shook his wife and children violently. This man realized the triviality of the provocations and wanted to correct his awful, un-Christian, barbaric behavior. He had prayed about it, but after a short break, he returned to his bad behavior. Now he wanted help, and his wife had come to support him.

I explained to this couple that we depend totally on God, but we also need to use whatever resources are available to us to do our part, and then God will do the rest. We discussed how important it was to keep moods manageable and to undercut anger long before it bursts out. This man needed to identify the causes of his anger and to act upon them. But he also needed to detect signals—"prodromal indicators"—that warned that he was about to blow up.

Well, this man had a hard time identifying such things, but apparently his wife didn't. She could tell when his anger was building and knew that he would soon lose control. At their next session, they told me their discovery, which they had already tested and so knew that it worked. This was the trick: whenever this man's wife sensed that his anger was building up, she would look straight into his eyes and, in a calm tone, say, "One hundred pesos!" They had agreed this nonsense expression would be the signal for him to step back, interrupt the process, and regain control.

In the Christian framework, this is only primary care—a step in the right direction. The definitive solution comes with a life that it is under the control of the Holy Spirit: "Those who live in accordance with the Spirit have their minds set on what the Spirit desires. The mind of sinful man is death, but the mind controlled by the Spirit is life and peace" (Romans 8:5, 6).

Disturbing thinking

People can tell when our thoughts become distressing. *"La cara es el espejo del alma"* (The face is the mirror of the soul), is a widely known and much-used Spanish proverb. Daniel 4 relates Nebuchadnezzar's dream of an enormous tree, visible from the ends of the earth, that is cut down and its branches, leaves, and fruit scattered so that only the stump and its roots are left. This dream also pictures a man's heart being changed into a beast's heart, causing him to behave totally like an animal. When the prophet Daniel heard the account, he was "greatly perplexed for a time, and his thoughts terrified him" (Daniel 4:19). His face must have revealed his feelings very explicitly, because the king—who was himself very afraid—stopped thinking of himself for a moment, focused on Daniel instead, and encouraged him not to be alarmed.

Distressful thoughts, unless temporary and soon resolved as Daniel's were, may lead to maladaptive behavior. That is why the cognitive-behavior approach says it's so important to avoid the wrong kind of thinking. But we also need to recognize something that the cognitive-behavior approach doesn't emphasize—the fact that behavior and external circumstances, in turn, may cause the wrong kind of thinking. That's why a Christian approach to avoiding evil should include both the internal and the external.

Christopher Barlett and Christopher Rodeheffer, from Iowa State University and Kansas State University respectively, studied the effects of computer games on aggressive thoughts and feelings.[2] The subjects were seventy-four college students (thirty-nine male, thirty-five female) who were randomly assigned to play one of three games: *Conflict: Desert Storm* (violent and realistic), *Star Wars: Battlefront 2* (violent but unrealistic), or *Hard Hitter Tennis* (nonviolent). Those young men and women who played the violent, realistic game displayed the highest levels of aggressive thoughts, aggressive feelings, and heart beats per minute during the four times they were assessed. Those who played the violent, unrealistic game ranked next in aggressiveness, and the players of the nonviolent game ranked lowest. It was clear that in this case, behavior caused thinking, rather than the reverse.

A large-scale study carried out by Ayman Fanous and his associates from the Institute of Psychiatric and Behavioral Genetics at the Virginia Commonwealth University aimed to discover the variables affecting suicidal ideation—thoughts of death and self-harm.[3] The subjects were female twins from the Virginia Twin Registry. They were an average of twenty-nine years of age at the beginning of the study and thirty-six years of age at its end. Some 2,164 women (1,082 twin pairs) were interviewed initially, and there were three other interviews separated by at least a year. Even with some loss of participants (1,942 women completed all the interviews), the results showed that suicidal ideas and thoughts of self-harm didn't come entirely from within. Certain external variables were also able to predict those thoughts. These variables included sexual abuse in childhood, loss of job, cocaine misuse, low levels of education, low religiosity, low altruism, loss of a dear one, assault, and financial problems.

This study reveals that certain thought processes—suicidal in this case—are clearly affected by circumstances and external factors. Consequently, it would also be reasonable to believe that favorable conditions and behaviors would bring about favorable thinking. What are those behaviors? The book *Developing a Healthy Mind*[4] suggests that a lifestyle guided by universal principles and values, such as honesty, responsibility, justice, respect for others, integrity, and truthfulness, supports a healthy thinking style.

Wholesome thinking

According to the apostle Peter's own statement, he wrote both his letters to the Christian church to "stimulate . . . wholesome thinking" (2 Peter 3:1). The King James Version translates this expression as "stir up . . . pure minds by way of remembrance." The emphasis is placed upon some sort of cognitive task—perhaps including thinking, understanding, reasoning, comparing and contrasting, memorizing, observing cause-effect relationships, and applying principles to practice—all around the messages from the prophets and the gospel of Jesus Christ (verse 2). Peter was appealing to all his readers to stick to Scripture as the sure way of keeping a safe mental outlook.

John Selden (1584–1654) was one of the most learned individuals who ever lived. His library is estimated to have contained some eight thousand volumes, a vast number for the time. Archbishop Usher was by Selden's side when he was on his deathbed, and Usher heard him say, "I have surveyed most of the learning that is among the sons of men, and my study is filled with books and manuscripts on various subjects. But at present, I cannot recollect any passage out of all my books and papers whereon I can rest my soul, save this from the sacred Scriptures." Then he recited Titus 2:11–14, a passage about the blessed hope and the glorious appearing of Jesus Christ.

We can say the same about 2 Peter 3. For all we know, the eighteen verses making up this chapter are the last that Peter wrote before his death. What was the subject of his last message? It was the second advent of Jesus, the blessed hope for all Christians. Peter urged the believers to focus their minds on the final event in spite of scoffers, erring teachers, and cruel persecution. (We need to remember that Peter's letters were written around A.D. 60–70, right in the middle of the worst of Nero's rule.) Peter transmitted the certainty that hope in Jesus' return would offer peace and meaning in the midst of tribulation.

What are we to do to cultivate wholesome thinking? In the words of the apostle Paul, the answer is to "let the peace of Christ rule in your hearts" (Colossians 3:15). In fact, the first seventeen verses of Colossians 3 can be considered a set of useful principles that hold a perfect balance between mind/heart and practice. Notice the expressions Paul used: "set your hearts," "set your minds," "rid yourselves of . . . anger, rage, malice" (all emotional states), "clothe yourselves with compassion," "forgive," "put on love," "let the peace of Christ rule in your hearts," "be thankful," and "let the word of Christ dwell in you."

Here are some of the principles of holy living that we can extract from Colossians 3:1–17:

- Christ is above all earthly things.
- Christ is the Source of life.
- There is clear distinction between the old self and the new self.
- In Christ, there are no personal distinctions of any kind whatsoever.

- Brotherly love is the ruling principle among God's people.
- Christ is the only One capable of bringing true peace to our minds.
- Christians must be thankful to God.

My family and I were visiting a church where we knew no one, and stayed for the potluck after the service. Most participants were adults, and soon our fourteen-year-old son approached us with words that are always said with a peculiar intonation: "This is boring!" My wife was quick to react; "Boring is a state of mind," she said. "Choose *not* to be bored!" Our son put on a perplexed face, but his mother's recommendation must have given him some food for thought because he didn't complain for the rest of the potluck, and we saw him conversing with a few people around him. Yes, we can choose what to think. In fact, we can submit our thoughts to Jesus Christ to attain peace of mind.

If you find your thoughts disturbing, or they are resulting in undesirable behavior, bring them to Jesus. You may discover that they become true, noble, right, pure, lovely, admirable, excellent, and praiseworthy (see Philippians 4:8).

1. Ellen G. White, *Reflecting Christ* (Hagerstown, Md.: Review and Herald®, 1985), 308.

2. Christopher P. Barlett and Christopher Rodeheffer, "Effect of Realism on Extended Violent and Nonviolent Video Game Play on Aggressive Thoughts, Feelings, and Physiological Arousal," *Aggressive Behavior* 35 (2009): 213–224.

3. Ayman H. Fanous et al., "The Prediction of Thoughts of Death or Self-Harm in a Population-based Sample of Female Twins," *Psychological Medicine* 34 (2004): 301–312.

4. Julián Melgosa, *Developing a Healthy Mind* (Madrid: Safeliz, 2007), 17.

CHAPTER 7

Depression

Sharon* was seventy-five when her husband died. After his death, she developed symptoms similar to those she had experienced half a century before, when she gave birth to her daughter and suffered postpartum depression. In addition to profound sadness, she complained of having no energy and no appetite and of not being able to get a good night's sleep. She began to feel that she could no longer handle the tasks that she had cared for previously, and the thought of adding to her burden the matters her husband had been responsible for, such as banking, insurance, and the maintenance of her car, overwhelmed her. Additionally, though her religion had always been important to her, she no longer wanted to pray.

Sharon knew that she needed medications to alleviate the terrible pain of depression she was experiencing, and she had no objection to placing herself under the care of a doctor to obtain them. But she also knew that psychiatric drugs weren't the complete answer to her problem and that she'd also need counseling. The doctor she saw helped her find the right kind of medicine, and she recommended a good counselor who had worked extensively with older people.

This counselor, a middle-aged woman, was so warm and sympathetic that Sharon soon took a liking to her weekly appointments. There she could talk about her past and her current life and all the feelings and emotions she experienced. The therapist was a good listener and knew how to

---

*A pseudonym.

ask questions that encouraged Sharon to talk more.

Just talking with the assurance that the person listening cared about her and that their conversation was strictly confidential helped Sharon to start feeling better. Her self-confidence grew, and she felt the desire to learn the new tasks that her widowhood demanded. Once again, she found enjoyment in going out, relating to people, and eating, and she recovered from her insomnia. The counselor also sent a volunteer who helped Sharon understand the paperwork her husband used to do and who kept visiting her regularly to make sure she was on top of things. And as soon as Sharon felt a bit better, she took up prayer and Scripture reading again, which also helped her immensely.

The number of people who experience depression has been growing dramatically since World War II. Depression is now the most common mental disorder. According to the World Health Organization, depression affects about 121 million people worldwide and is the number one cause of disability in terms of the number of years lived with disability by the people who contract it.[1] In the United States alone, it touches between 10 and 25 percent of women and between 5 and 12 percent of men.[2] This problem affects people of all ages, classes, races, and backgrounds, as well as the myriads of family members and friends who live near the afflicted person.

Symptoms of major depression include depressive mood, absence of interest in or pleasure from favorite things, lack of energy, lack of appetite, sleep disturbances, motor retardation, feelings of low self-esteem or guilt, cognitive limitations, and suicidal thoughts or behaviors. (Some 10 to 15 percent of people with major depression manage to take their lives.) A solid diagnosis can be made when someone experiences five or more of these symptoms persistently for more than two weeks. Just three or four of the symptoms can make a person feel miserable without being officially depressed.

Religion and depression

Many secular psychotherapists used to charge that religion was a cause of depression. They argued that guilt-prone believers suffered from depression because religions impose rules that people can't keep, and religion minimizes the inner goodness of people and completely ruins their self-esteem. This perspective has changed considerably. In the past two decades, a large body of research on the positive effects of religion on physical and mental health (depression included) has become available, and the benefits of religion are now fairly well established.[3]

For example, a recent issue of *Geriatrics,* a medical journal for physicians, gerontologists, and geriatric nurses, contained an article titled "Incorporating Religion and Spirituality to Improve Care for Anxiety and Depression in Older Adults."[4] The authors discuss evidence showing the benefits of discussing religious/spiritual activities with older patients, and they suggest specific ways to integrate religion/spirituality into the treatment prescribed—among them, promoting thoughts of gratitude, encouraging forgiveness, asking patients to let go of hurt and anger, inviting them to resume religious attendance if depression has made them interrupt such practices, and so forth. The journal even published with this article an advertisement inviting doctors to attend a continuing education course on prayer and spirituality offered by the American College of Physicians.

While religion is helpful in preventing depression and other problems, it may be so only under certain circumstances. When I lived in England, I heard of the research on health and religion conducted by Dr. Montagu Barker at Bristol University. Since that university was just a two- or three-hour drive away, a colleague and I went there one day to listen to a couple of Dr. Barker's lectures. He reported on the results of the many studies emerging at that time that showed the connection between religious practices and physical health (longer life, reduced risk of arteriosclerosis and heart disease, faster recovery from illness, etc.) as well as mental-emotional-behavioral health (decreased incidence of depression and anxiety, a hopeful outlook, and low risk of criminal behavior and of substance dependence). However, Dr. Barker pointed out that it was people with a firm commitment to their religion who got these dividends, not the nominal members. In fact, occasional churchgoers who didn't have a firm commitment obtained fewer health benefits than those who didn't attend at all!

Depressed people in the Bible

The Bible doesn't contain enough details about symptoms and their incidence for us to know for sure whether the characters in its stories suffered from depression. But it does tell us enough about the symptoms of some of the characters to enable us to surmise that they would probably have met the criteria for depression as understood today. The Bible has preserved these examples so we can gain insight into how God can help the brokenhearted today as He did the men and women of the past. Let's consider a few examples.

- *Hannah.* First Samuel 1 offers a good picture of Hannah's emotional condition. We are told of a number of things that reveal her deep discouragement. The Lord had closed Hannah's womb (verse 5). In that cultural context, motherhood was a clear sign of divine blessing, and its absence, a sign of a curse. Hannah's condition may have given her a sense of guilt and inferiority—both feelings typically found in depressive patients.

- The maternal differences between Hannah and Peninnah must have mortified Hannah, but to top it all, Peninnah purposefully provoked Hannah (verse 6), even though she knew that by law her first son would receive a double share of the inheritance (see Deuteronomy 21:15–17). To understand Peninnah's behavior fully, we must remember that Elkanah, the husband of both women, loved Hannah more than he did Peninnah—a typical complication in polygamous families.

- Hannah wept bitterly over her infertility (1 Samuel 1:7, 10). In part, she cried because of Peninnah's provocation, but—as indicated by her praying at the temple—her sorrow was rooted in other matters too. Weeping is one of the most common symptoms of depression.

- She wouldn't eat (verse 7). Loss of appetite is a common sign of depression, and Hannah must have displayed it more than once, for Elkanah asked in frustration, "Why don't you eat?"

- Hannah experienced bitterness of soul (verse 10). Her deep sadness may have been what we refer today as depressive mood, which may have worsened when Elkanah showed he didn't understand by asking, "Why are you downhearted? Don't I mean more to you than ten sons?" (verse 8).

- Hannah spoke of "your servant's misery" (verse 11) and said she was "deeply troubled" (verse 15) and "in great anguish and grief" (verse 16). It's likely that these expressions refer to the deep sadness that characterizes clinical depression.

- Hannah's face was downcast. Her facial spark was gone. She was sad until Eli blessed her (see verses 17, 18).

The solution to Hannah's condition began with the comforting words of Eli: " 'Go in peace, and may the God of Israel grant you what you have asked of him' " (verse 17). Scripture says her troubled countenance changed and she ate something. Notice that Hannah's mental healing came even before her request was granted. Eventually, her deeply felt prayer was answered—she was granted the privilege of being the mother of one of the greatest prophets ever. And then she had three other sons and two daughters (see 1 Samuel 2:21).

Elijah. By divine intervention, through great miracles that occurred in the midst of adversity, Elijah went through a spectacular series of victories (1 Kings 16–18). But then we see the prophet taking an emotional downturn (see chapter 19).

- Having won the crucial battle against Baal, Elijah could have gone on to fight the final battle. But instead, he experienced intense fear (1 Kings 19:3) and ran away. He may have thought that God wasn't treating him fairly when He allowed a death warrant to be placed on his head after his long battle against evil.
- He prayed for God to take his life (verse 4). Thoughts of death are quite common in depressive people. Some try to take their lives, and some who try are successful. Elijah didn't attempt suicide, but he thought death preferable to the emotional pain that continued to plague him.
- On two occasions Elijah spoke of how discouraged he felt because the Israelites rejected God's covenants, destroyed His altars, and killed His prophets (verses 10, 14). This must have been a significant source of the depression he felt after his experience on Mount Carmel.

Heaven's treatment of Elijah's symptoms began with an angel cooking a meal for him and then sending him for serious physical exercise. He was healed through the encounter with God that ended in a gentle whisper. God's assurance that there were " 'seven thousand in Israel—all whose knees have not bowed down to Baal' " (1 Kings 19:18) must also have been therapeutic to Elijah, who had believed that he was the only remaining faithful one.

David. Israel's shepherd-king died at the age of seventy. Although his life wasn't particularly long by today's standards, it was full of action and excitement. From his early days on, David faced a great deal of emotional turmoil because he was the youngest in his family and later the object of obsessive persecution by King Saul. When David became king over Judah, he continued to experience a great deal of mental agony—at that time because of his own mistakes, the harassment of his enemies, and trouble in his family.

Mental and Emotional Health

The book of Psalms contains many passages that are precious jewels to the brokenhearted. In part, they're attractive because of their rich language, but a greater reason is their author's experience in heartache. In these psalms, David wrote of a loving God who is the Balm needed by those who suffer.

David himself recognized that his experience with life and with God would be useful to other sinners. When the prophet Nathan came to him after his adultery with Bathsheba, David wrote a psalm in which he fully admitted his transgression and asked God for forgiveness. He prayed, "Restore to me the joy of your salvation," and said, "then I will teach transgressors your ways, and sinners will turn back to you" (Psalm 51:12, 13). Let's look at a few of David's states of mind as expressed in Psalm 42.*

- David's tears were copious (verse 3). He tells us that they have been his "meat day and night" (KJV). In the context, it seems obvious that these were tears of sorrow.
- Past events disturbed him (verse 4). At this time, David was probably in exile, and he missed the temple services. Memories from the past do tend to disturb—in one way or another—those suffering from depression.
- He was experiencing inner turmoil (verse 5). He says that his soul is "downcast" and "disturbed within me," revealing the spiritual pain inside that is comparable to someone going through physical affliction.
- Insurmountable barriers surrounded him (verse 7). David uses waterfalls as a metaphor to express the clamor of his circumstances. These waters aren't mere noisemakers; they contain impassable power—the waves breaking over him.
- He had the impression that God had left him (verse 9). The internal tension and the pressure from his enemies make David mourn. The trial is of such intensity that he wonders, as do many in the midst of depression, where God is.
- His emotional pain produces physical symptoms (verse 10): "My bones suffer mortal agony as my foes taunt me."
- He didn't receive the social support he needed (verses 3, 10). Loving people are a good source of healing to the brokenhearted.

---

*While the heading on this psalm identifies it as belonging to the Sons of Korah, some commentators consider David to be its author.—Editor.

However, the people surrounding David were not only unsupportive, but they were positively venomous as they kept asking, "Where is your God?"

The solution to David's problem comes from God, but David needs to take the initiative. He decides to remember God even from a distant land, to put his hope in him, and to praise him in spite of his troubles. As a result, the Lord directs His love toward David during the day, and at night, He sends a song to his heart. And in response, David sends a prayer to the God of his life (see verse 8).

Hezekiah. This king witnessed a number of remarkable events and victories attributable only to God. Then he became sick unto death, a fate confirmed by the terrible words of Isaiah: " 'Put your house in order because you are going to die; you will not recover' " (Isaiah 38:1). But Hezekiah prayed for a miracle, and God answered his prayer, granting him an additional fifteen years of life. Later, Hezekiah wrote of the emotional journey he experienced when he thought his death was sure. His words of despair are recorded in Isaiah 38. Hezekiah's agony was not a silent one. He wept bitterly (verse 3), comparing the pain he felt to that which he would have experienced if a lion had broken all his bones (verse 13)! He said he chattered like a crane or a swallow, mourned like a dove, and his eyes grew weak (KJV); but, in his agony, he turned to God and prayed, "I am troubled; O Lord, come to my aid!" (verse 14). And God answered his prayer.

Jeremiah. This prophet witnessed the chaos his nation went through at the time Nebuchadnezzar devastated Jerusalem. When Jeremiah was " ' "only a child," ' " God called him to be a prophet (Jeremiah 1:7). However, his appeals to his fellow citizens seemed useless; nobody wanted to follow God's instruction. So he was a witness when Israel, instead of winning victories, disintegrated morally and suffered physical destruction. He saw Nebuchadnezzar besiege Jerusalem and then sack the city, taking its citizens captive to Babylon. Then the remnant that was left forced him to flee with them to Egypt. Jeremiah's lamentations vividly show his agony.

- The mental distress is both external and internal (Lamentations 1:20). Jeremiah expresses his condition with words such as " 'distressed,' " " 'disturbed,' " and " 'torment.' " The pressure comes not only from outside sources (" 'the sword bereaves' "), but also from within (" 'I am in torment within' ").

- He experiences darkness (Lamentations 3:1, 6). In describing their condition, those suffering from depression frequently picture themselves as in darkness rather than light.
- Jeremiah's emotional pain is so intense that it affects his physical being (verses 4, 16). He notices his skin and flesh growing old and feels as though his bones and teeth are broken.
- He feels like he can't escape the agony (verses 5, 7). He speaks of being "besieged," "walled," "weighed . . . down with chains," and "surrounded . . . with bitterness and hardship"—words and phrases that convey hopelessness, a common feature of depression.
- Jeremiah has no supportive social network (verse 14). He's the laughingstock of his own people—one of the worst consequences depressed people experience.
- His thoughts and memories are focused on the negative (verses 17–20). Jeremiah seems to share what is commonly found in people subject to depression—a selective memory, focused on the somber aspects of the past. The text indicates that Jeremiah has lost his hope in God, together with a sense of God's splendor. He remembers instead his affliction, wandering, bitterness, and gall, and, as a result, his soul is downcast.

When Jeremiah reached his turning point (verse 21), he decided to have hope, to recognize God's unfailing love and great faithfulness, and to wait for Him, because "the LORD is good to those whose hope is in him, to the one who seeks him; it is good to wait quietly for the salvation of the LORD" (verses 25, 26).

What to do about depression

Major depression is a disorder that can be treated with the help of medical and psychological professionals. Self-help measures are crucial both to preventing this problem and to support whatever intervention is applied. Gaining full recovery requires the cooperation of the depressed person and sometimes of that person's family. In what follows, I present briefly a number of these self-help measures and the principles behind them, which can be found in the Bible.

Talk. Talking in a safe environment to someone who truly cares is among the most effective ways to treat depression as well as other mental disorders. The work of remembering and expressing one's feelings brings organization and relief. Often, even though nothing material has changed and the counselor hasn't offered direct input, the outlook of people suffering from depression improves after a therapeutic session in which they have talked freely. Discussion of one's situation and feelings tends to make them look much less threatening and much more manageable.

People who can find the energy to write have found doing so to be very helpful. A client once told me, "I think I survived those years of torment fighting with my disease because I kept a journal where I wrote about the struggles I was going through." These days, many find blogging therapeutic. It allows people to unload their burdens and also provides caring listeners—trusted friends who have been given access.

Praying—talking in confidence with God—also brings healing. To people of faith, prayer is a way to escape discouragement—and the Listener guarantees confidentiality, full attention, and permanent availability. In Psalm 39, David presents the results of talking to the Lord in contrast to withholding one's thoughts from Him. "When I was silent and still," he said, "my anguish increased" (verse 2). But after he prayed for understanding, he told God, " 'My hope is in you' " (verse 7).

Search for social support. Depressed people tend to remain isolated. That's why treatment plans typically include activity programs tailored to their needs and strengths. The professional literature contains abundant evidence that, if someone takes people who are depressed out of the house into a social context and helps them become active (within reason!), they can recover. This is especially true when the activity includes *helping someone else directly or indirectly.* Such activities not only combat recurring thoughts and feelings of helplessness, but also promote the sense of satisfaction and well-being that comes from helping others. This offers a great practical defense against depression and also fulfills the moral imperative Paul gave, "Carry each other's burdens, and in this way you will fulfill the law of Christ" (Galatians 6:2).

Confess and forgive. In "The Tell-Tale Heart," Edgar Allen Poe tells a story in which a man plans and carries out the murder of the old man with whom he lives. The assassin acts so carefully that no investigator would ever be able to trace what he has done. When he has killed the old man, he carefully hides parts of the corpse under the flooring of his house.

The next day, three police officers come to inspect the premises. Though they search thoroughly, they find no trace of the murder. As the officers chat casually before they depart, the murderer hears a heartbeat that becomes increasingly loud. Convinced that he's hearing the heart of the murdered man beating loudly beneath the floor and that the policemen can hear it, too, the murderer confesses his crime. However, the sound he was hearing was actually that of his own heart, which was pounding hard because of his fear.

Some people are depressed because they—deservedly—feel guilty. On the other hand, people also feel depressed because they won't forgive the offenses of others. Confessing, forgiving, and being forgiven are intimately related. We cannot receive God's forgiveness when we're not willing to forgive others. That's at least in part what the prayer Jesus taught us to pray says, "Forgive us our debts, as we forgive our debtors" (Matthew 6:12, KJV). In Psalm 32, David wrote of the importance of forgiveness:

> Day and night
>   your hand was heavy upon me;
> my strength was sapped
>   as in the heat of summer.
> Then I acknowledged my sin to you. . . .
> And you forgave
>   the guilt of my sin (verses 4, 5).

Think appropriately. Aaron T. Beck, a Yale-trained psychiatrist, founded the cognitive-behavioral approach explained in the previous chapter. His clinical experience led him to believe that most people who are depressed think poorly of themselves (I'm no good), the world (everything is working against me), and the future (the situation will never improve). Beck calls this attitude "catastrophic thinking."

The Bible offers us a better way of thinking—a better outlook, a more positive perspective on ourselves. We are created in God's image, with authority over creation. And God's traits are still within us, though marred by sin. Jesus Christ offered Himself as a sacrifice so we could have a new life and eternal salvation. By God's grace, we have the potential to achieve great things in serving others and for the glory of God.

How should we view the world? Although it is true that the world is evil and rotten, it still contains many good, noble, and admirable things for us to contemplate (Philippians 4:8). Furthermore, we can admit the existence of evil without despair because we know that eventually it will be eradicated.

How should we view the future? We can believe that it offers us a great array of wonderful experiences. The Bible is full of promises that God watches over His children, and it insists on the reality of salvation—a powerful "stronghold in time of trouble" (Psalm 37:39).

Keep up hope. An American soldier captured by the Vietnamese in an ambush, was tortured in various ways. After the ordeal, his condition was deplorable, but although he could have died at any moment, he managed to stay alive. Then his captors told him that they would free him on a date that they specified. The soldier grew stronger and happier as that day approached. However, on the day when he was to be liberated, his captors told him that they wouldn't free him after all—that they had purposely deceived him and would never set him free. Within just a few days, the young prisoner died. Hope had brought life to him, and the lack of hope brought death.

In the last chapter of the book of Micah, the prophet describes a period of total chaos in the history of Israel: famine, violence, deception, corruption, hatred, abuse, betrayal, family dishonor, and neighborly mistrust. But in the midst of all this adversity, Micah was full of hope. He wrote, "But as for me, *I watch in hope for the LORD, I wait for God my Savior; my God will hear me*" (Micah 7:7; emphasis added).

If you are discouraged, place your hope in the promises in Scripture. Even in times of adversity for all levels of society—times such as those Micah experienced—you can hold on to the assurance that "the LORD is close to the brokenhearted and saves those who are crushed in spirit" (Psalm 34:18).

---

1. See www.who.int/mental_heath/management/depression/definition/en/index.html.

2. *Diagnostic and Statistical Manual of Mental Disorders,* American Psychiatric Association, 341. These estimates refer only to those cases that have resulted in a firm diagnosis of major depression.

3. See Harold G. Koenig, Michael E. McCullough, and David B. Larson, *Handbook of Religion and Health* (Oxford: Oxford University Press, 2001). See also Michael E. McCullough and Timothy Smith, "Religion and Health: Depressive Symptoms and Mortality as Case Studies," *Handbook of the Sociology of Religion,* ed. Michele Dillon (Cambridge: Cambridge University Press, 2003).

4. Laura L. Phillips et al., "Incorporating Religion and Spirituality to Improve Care for Anxiety and Depression in Older Adults," *Geriatrics* 64 (2009): 15–18.

CHAPTER 8

Resilience

Helen Keller was born to a wealthy family in Tuscumbia, Alabama, in 1880. When she was only nineteen months old, she was struck by an illness diagnosed at the time as brain fever that left her deaf and blind. As a result, her early childhood was disorderly and she had little enrichment from her environment. But when Helen was six, her parents hired Anne Sullivan, a twenty-year-old teacher who had been blind herself but had recovered her sight through surgery. Anne put one of Helen's hands in the stream flowing from a pump and with her finger wrote the letters W-A-T-E-R in Helen's other hand. Then Helen realized that communication was possible; she could learn about the things she encountered.

In time, Helen learned to read raised print and to write. When Anne told Helen about a deaf-blind girl in Norway who had learned to speak, Helen indicated that she wanted to learn how to talk, too, so she was taken to the Horace Mann School to receive speech lessons. Eventually, she attended Radcliffe College, from which she graduated cum laude with a B.A. degree. And from then on, she led an active literary life, publishing several books and contributing regularly to magazines and newspapers on the topics of blindness, deafness, social issues, women's issues, and religion. Helen received numerous awards, distinctions, and honorary doctoral degrees. Her interesting and fruitful life, which has brought inspiration and blessings to many, ended in 1968.

Helen Keller was a highly resilient woman. She wrote, "I have never believed that my limitations were in any sense punishments or accidents.

Resilience

If I had held such a view, I could never have exerted the strength to overcome them. I thank God for my handicaps; for through them, I have found myself, my work, and my God."[1]

Resilience is the ability to endure illness, change, or misfortune and bounce back with added strength to attain goals unthinkable before the crisis. Resilience has been under serious study in recent years. There is something about human suffering that makes some people emerge with an extra measure of power and strength.

Instances in which people have responded to experiences of adversity with outstanding achievements are not isolated or rare. In 1964, Victor Goertzel, a research psychologist trained at the University of California and at the University of Michigan, and his wife, Mildred, a high school teacher and professional writer, published a book titled *Cradles of Eminence.*[2] They selected four hundred individuals whom they judged to be eminent based upon the number of biographies written about them. Their list included such people as Franklin Roosevelt, Mahatma Gandhi, Winston Churchill, Albert Schweitzer, Theodore Roosevelt, Albert Einstein, Nelson Rockefeller, Leo Tolstoy, Mark Twain, William James, and Sigmund Freud. Then the Goertzels spent several years analyzing the environment in which these people grew up.

Although they found that some of these prominent people had grown up in warm, supportive environments, they also found that an unexpectedly high proportion of them had hated school and school teachers and had grown up with opinionated parents, failure-prone fathers, and/or domineering mothers. Many others had physical defects or disabilities, and, in fact, many of them said that it was their handicaps that had motivated them to excel.

In 2004, Ted Goertzel, Victor and Mildred's son, published a second edition of the original work, adding three hundred more cases from recent years.[3] Among the personalities added were Robert Kennedy, Nelson Mandela, Hermann Hesse, Simone de Beauvoir, Walt Disney, Teresa of Calcutta, Tiger Woods, Oprah Winfrey, Barbara Streisand, Hillary Clinton, and Bill Gates. Overall, these more contemporary people, who had clear goals and very high internal motivations to attain them, came from backgrounds similar to those of the people featured in the first edition.

There are millions of people today who are enduring severe illness, the loss of a dear one, divorce, unemployment, poverty, single-parenting, violence (domestic, criminal, or the result of terrorism), natural disaster, and war. Many a survivor of such conditions will resiliently rise with enhanced power, not just to become wealthy or a successful professional, but to enjoy sound mental health and happiness. This is possible only because a loving Creator has given the beings He created the mechanisms and resources to recover from setbacks and build happy lives.

The Bible contains many references to resilient individuals. Once the severe adversity that was holding them back ended, God used them as channels through which He could accomplish His mission. Studying the lives of such men and women may help us to face our own stressful situations by depending upon the invincible power of God.

Resilient men in the Bible

Noah lived so long that his life is measured in centuries, so he must have experienced all kinds of sorrows. We are told of a few: He witnessed the growing corruption of God's children. He faced the heavy demands of building an ark while being mocked by virtually everyone. He witnessed the decadence of his own descendants after the Flood. And he even had to curse one of his own sons.

Abraham left his country, his people, and the household of his father to start a journey with an unknown destination. He faced a multitude of issues related to his wife's barrenness and God's promise of numerous descendants. He experienced significant tensions with members of his family and household. And he experienced one of the hardest tests of loyalty— the sacrifice of his own teenage son, the son of promise.

Moses endured endless pressures: His Hebrew origin raised tension in the court of Egypt. His killing of the Egyptian foreman forced him to flee in fear and guilt. His negotiations with Pharaoh were difficult and accompanied with terrible plagues. And, for nearly forty years, he had to face the constant rebellion of the Israelites.

In the New Testament, we find that John the Baptist, the forerunner of the Messiah, and, according to Jesus, the greatest of the prophets, who lived a humble, committed, and sacrificial life. Despite that, though, his ministry obtained very partial results, and he was unjustly thrown into prison, where his faith was shaken, as we see in the fact that he sent his disciples to ask Jesus, " 'Are you the one who was to come, or should we expect someone else?' " (Matthew 11:3).

The apostle Paul's lifestyle changed radically after his conversion. On several occasions, he went to prison because of his faith. He was beaten severely a few times and stoned once. He traveled extensively under perilous conditions, while bearing the constant pressure of concern and responsibility for the early Christian communities.

All of these men, and many others mentioned in the Bible, suffered intensely. But after each trial, they emerged stronger. They possessed resilience that comes only from God.

Let's take a closer look at two of the most resilient men in the Bible: Job and Joseph.

Job. This servant of the Lord was "blameless and upright; he feared God and shunned evil" (Job 1:1). Yet he was subjected to a severe test that was made even more difficult to endure because most people of his day believed that suffering was the direct result of a person's wrongdoings. While this test was very personal, it also had universal implications; when Satan claimed that Job feared the Lord only because the Lord blessed and protected him, it became a test in which the forces of evil confronted those of good. With God's permission, Satan destroyed Job's wealth, family, and health. The evil one arranged for enemies to steal Job's livestock and his servants, and he sent fire to destroy Job's crops and workers. Then he sent a powerful wind from the desert to collapse the house where Job's children were feasting, killing them all. And finally, Satan afflicted Job with painful sores that covered his entire body. Job responded to all of this with complete submission to the Lord's will. He said,

> "Naked I came from my mother's womb,
>   and naked I will depart.
> The LORD gave and the LORD has taken away;
>   may the name of the LORD be praised" (Job 1:21).

But the trials that came to Job didn't end with his losses of wealth, children, and health. The social network he was left with failed him too. In the midst of his suffering, his wife undercut him further, saying, " 'Are you still holding on to your integrity? Curse God and die!' " (Job 2:9). And the three friends who came to comfort him blamed him for his misfortune, which didn't help him at all.

Job's experience is the supreme example of patience, long-suffering, and perseverance. His attitude models the ideal reaction of a believer when facing adversity, especially when it's undeserved. James referred to Job: "Brothers, as an example of patience in the face of suffering, take the prophets who spoke in the name of the Lord. As you know, we consider blessed those who have persevered. You have heard of Job's perseverance and have seen what the Lord finally brought about. The Lord is full of compassion and mercy" (James 5:10, 11). The lesson to which James pointed is twofold: (1) hold on to hope in a God who wants the best for you and is compassionate and merciful, and (2) understand that what God does is always good in the long run. That's why the psalmist said many a time: "Wait on the Lord."

When I was president of the Adventist International Institute of Advanced Studies (AIIAS) in the Philippines, I often thought that when someone made an appointment to see me, it meant trouble. Of course, that wasn't always the case. At least I knew for sure that when Dr. Ken Mulzac, professor of Old Testament, came to see me, it wasn't necessarily to lay a problem on me. A pastoral prayer and a few words of encouragement always accompanied the visit.

Dr. Mulzac developed cancer. I'll never forget the answer he gave when I asked him how he was coping with his illness. He said, *"Dios aprieta pero no ahoga!"* (God tightens but does not choke)—a Spanish proverb usually spoken to encourage someone undergoing difficulties. Dr. Mulzac fought the disease for a number of years, but now he's resting until the voice of Jesus awakens him.

We may have to endure a lot of pain, but we can always have the assurance that God has something much better in store for us. Job's response to his friends' philosophical arguments reveals that he believed this. He said,

"I know that my Redeemer lives,
    and that in the end he will stand upon the earth.
And after my skin has been destroyed,
    yet in my flesh I will see God" (Job 19:25, 26).

Joseph. Jacob's favorite son had at least two significantly painful experiences that completely changed the direction of his life. The first involved his brothers. Joseph may have lacked tact when he told his brothers about his dreams and displayed his many-colored coat, but the price they made him pay was out of proportion to his offense: they determined to kill him in cold blood. Reuben intervened and prevented the murder, but then Joseph's brothers stripped the special coat off of him and sold him to a caravan of Ishmaelite merchants, who, in turn, sold Joseph as a slave in Egypt.

Then Joseph was unjustly put in prison. While he was faithfully serving Potiphar, the captain of Pharaoh's guard, Potiphar's wife tried repeatedly to seduce him. Eventually, enraged by Joseph's rejections of her advances, she accused him of attempting to assault her, and he was thrown in prison.

Both instances resulted in very unfair actions that Joseph didn't deserve. However, he bounced back from them, and, in the end, they opened the path that led Joseph to a position in the government of Egypt second only to that of Pharaoh himself. There Joseph was able to fulfill the great mission of saving many people from death, including his own kin.

Resilient women in the Bible

Rachel, a daughter of Laban, was a beautiful woman who grew up in a home that contained idols. Her father practiced divination and often cheated others, including Rachel and Jacob, whom she eventually married. Once married, she suffered for many more years because she couldn't get pregnant and because of the rivalry that existed between her and Leah, her sister and co-wife. Eventually, she did have children—Joseph and Benjamin.

Ruth was a citizen of Moab, a region of pagan people who worshiped gods that, in some cases, required human sacrifices. She married Mahlon, son of Elimelech and Naomi, Jewish immigrants who left their home in Israel because of a famine. Ruth soon became widowed, and though she'd had no children with her Israelite husband, she decided to stay with her mother-in-law, Naomi, who was also a widow with no living children. When Naomi returned to her home in Bethlehem, Ruth was at risk. She was a woman, a foreigner, and a young widow. But after some uncertainties and struggles, Boaz married her and provided her with a good life.

Hannah, whom we discussed in the previous chapter, suffered terribly because of her infertility and the provocations of Peninnah, and because of the resultant depression that made her so unhappy. But eventually, God blessed her abundantly—she had a son, Samuel, and then three more boys and two girls.

Mary, a young virgin, was entrusted with the great task of being the mother of the Messiah. The circumstances of her pregnancy brought her great difficulty, threatening even her relationship to her fiancé, Joseph. She delivered Jesus in very precarious circumstances, and in addition to poverty, the family had to live with the incredulity of many who questioned the circumstances of His birth. During Jesus' life, Mary had a limited understanding of His ministry and His role as the Messiah, yet "throughout His [Jesus'] life on earth she [Mary] was a partaker in His sufferings."[4]

All of these women had a divine calling and divine guidance, but all of them had to endure a great deal of suffering. Yet they each came through the trials with increased strength.

Let's study two other women who particularly exhibited resilience: Naomi and Esther.

Naomi. This ancestor of Jesus suffered a great deal for many years before she could make any sense of all her adversities. Here are some of the particular difficulties she experienced.

- She and her husband, Elimelech, together with their two sons, were forced to leave their country because of famine, which is a very different experience than leaving a place in search of new opportunities.
- Their destination, the land of Moab, was an agricultural area where they could survive, but that land was inhabited by an idolatrous people whose practices violated Jewish beliefs.
- Naomi's husband died, leaving her a widow with two boys to care for—a traumatizing event made worse because they were in a foreign land.
- Naomi's sons, Mahlon and Kilion, married local women, a fact that probably upset her and brought turmoil to the family, since Moses' law stipulated that Moabites couldn't enter the assembly of the Lord—and neither could their descendants up to the tenth generation (see Deuteronomy 23:3).
- Her sons, whose names mean "weakling" and "sickly," also died, leaving no living members of her immediate family—an incredibly tragic situation.

At this moment of deep tragedy, Ruth, Naomi's daughter-in-law, provided God-sent emotional support. Naomi must have been a remarkable woman to have inspired the devotion of her two daughters-in-law, especially Ruth, who accepted the God of Israel and made the firm decision to care for her mother-in-law for life, even in a land of traditional enemies. However, Naomi still had to go through a number of uncertainties and bitter steps before she could reach the end of her ordeal. Her statement to old friends in Bethlehem reveals some of her feelings: " 'Don't call me Naomi.' . . . 'Call me Mara, because the Almighty has made my life very bitter' " (Ruth 1:20). The two women returned in poverty, didn't know whether the connection with Boaz would work out, and were uncertain about the reaction of the kinsman-redeemer. But the story ends in a beautiful succession of events, and Naomi was pleased with the results (Ruth 4:16, 17).

Esther. The name of the Lord doesn't appear anywhere in the book of Esther. Yet this book is packed with God's providence and guidance. Esther, the central character, shows her resilience through how she handled a number of difficult circumstances.

- Esther had no mother or father. That's why her cousin Mordecai, a captive taken by King Nebuchadnezzar from Jerusalem to Babylon, adopted her. As Esther was growing up, she may have experienced prejudice because she was an orphan.
- When Esther was chosen as queen, Mordecai instructed her not to reveal her nationality or family background. This was a particularly difficult challenge, for the lifestyle in the court must have contrasted drastically with her Jewish faith and identity.
- Esther lived for some time with the fear of being identified as a Jew and the uncertainty of what would happen if she were found out.
- She informed the king that two of his personal officers were plotting to kill him. This must have been a source of stress for her, too, as the conspiracy had to be investigated, and if there wasn't sufficient evidence, she could have been killed.
- Perhaps the greatest pressure Esther bore was that of being the only one who could save the Jews of Babylon. At first she hesitated to intervene, but Mordecai put even more pressure on her: "If you remain silent at this time, relief and deliverance for the Jews will arise from another place, but you and your father's family will perish" (Esther 4:14).
- Anyone who entered the inner court uninvited while the king was there faced the penalty of death. And because the king hadn't called on Esther for quite a while, when she entered his throne room to save her people, she was risking death.

Despite all the pressure Esther faced, she didn't crumble. Instead, she devised a strategy to accomplish what seemed impossible. She asked all the Jews in Susa to assemble and fast for three days. Then she appeared before the king. Several miraculous events followed, and the Jewish population was saved as a result of Esther's mediation. The story is described in a most interesting way in the rest of the book of Esther (chapters 5–10).

God is still there

Even when we're under extreme pressure, God is still there and will accept and answer our prayers even if they're weak. The experience of Leonard Mulcahy confirms this conclusion. Leonard works at the Center for Psychiatric Rehabilitation at Boston University, and he teaches courses in fitness, wellness, and recovery. In an article published in the *Psychiatric Rehabilitation Journal,* he tells of his happy days of childhood and of his loving and caring family. He also says he was mentally healthy during his high school years, with plenty of friends and involvement in sports. But during his undergraduate days at the University of Massachusetts in Boston, he started to experience the symptoms of depression. He went through depressive moods, loneliness, suicidal ideation, and even paranoia—a symptom of psychosis that isn't normally found in depression. Leonard became suspicious of people. He thought that they were talking about him and laughing at him, and this reinforced his isolation.

Prayer was the turning point for Leonard. In telling his story, he said, "Resilience was a term I was not familiar with, but as my illness progressed, it became clear to me that I needed to be resilient in order to stay alive. I took a lot of time to pray. . . . I prayed for people in need and for people who were on the street and homeless. Prayer was my life saver and helped me to find a place for myself in this world."[5] When the symptoms of depression began to appear, Leonard told his therapist that he was too sick to pray. She encouraged him to pray anyway and to nurture his spiritual life.

Leonard worked as a volunteer in a soup kitchen, and he participated in prayer meetings regularly. He notes that "part of being resilient is being involved with others." He concluded his testimony this way: "Along my journey, which has been filled with many trials and tribulations, prayer has kept me moving forward down the right road of spiritual wholeness instead of self destruction and death. . . . Prayer allows me to be fully alive and spiritually awakened, which made all the difference."[6]

It isn't easy to affirm with the apostle Paul, "For Christ's sake, I *delight* in weaknesses, in insults, in hardships, in persecutions, in difficulties" (2 Corinthians 12:10; emphasis added). I still remember how I felt when, in secondary school, I failed my final exam in English (as a foreign language) three years in a row. I had studied enough, and I thought I was well prepared, but it seemed this wasn't the case. It is true that the assessment method was difficult and unreliable. We studied various subjects at our local school for a whole academic year, and then, in June, we went to an official examination hall on the other side of the city for a week of final tests.

Resilience

The stress meant that results could go either way. However, I didn't fail any of the other finals—only English, which I failed three years in a row.

I couldn't understand why I couldn't have my summers free from makeup work. But in the years since, I have become certain that the Lord caused it—or permitted it, or whatever—because it meant that I had to spend three extra summers studying English. Later, that additional study proved to be extremely useful because I needed to read English sources at college and to take graduate studies in the United States.

Even in the middle of difficulties, we must have faith that suffering will end and may have a purpose. One night, famous Welsh minister and Bible commentator Matthew Henry was assaulted by thieves, who took his money. Of that incident, Henry wrote in his journal, "Let me be thankful first, because I was never robbed before; second, because, although they took my purse, they did not take my life; third, because, although they took my all, it was not much; and fourth, because it was I who was robbed, not I who robbed."[7]

If you are going through affliction, you will undoubtedly find it very difficult to understand, but you may take courage from the knowledge that it is transitory and that

God is our refuge and strength,
    an ever-present help in trouble.
Therefore we will not fear, though the earth give way
    and the mountains fall into the heart of the sea,
though its waters roar and foam
    and the mountains quake with their surging (Psalm 46:1–3).

1. Helen Keller, *Light in My Darkness,* 2nd ed. (West Chester, Penn.: Chrysalis Books, 2000), 120.

2. Victor Goertzel and Mildred George Goertzel, *Cradles of Eminence* (New York: Little, Brown & Company, 1962).

3. Victor Goertzel, Mildred George Goertzel, Ted George Goertzel, and Ariel M. W. Hansen, *Cradles of Eminence,* 2nd ed. (Scottsdale, Ariz.: Great Potential Press, 2004).

4. Ellen G. White, *The Desire of Ages,* 90.

5. Leonard Mulcahy, "My Journey of Spirituality and Resilience," *Psychiatric Rehabilitation Journal* 30 (2007): 311, 312.

6. Ibid.

7. Paul Lee Tan, *Encyclopedia of 15,000 Illustrations,* entry 13179.

CHAPTER 9

Self-Esteem

Ever since her childhood, Gretchen* had problems with self-esteem. Yet she was capable, diligent, and pleasant to deal with. Her grades were consistently good all the way through college. When she graduated, she got a job in a large insurance company, and a short time later, she set up her own agency.

After just one year of operation, Gretchen hired an assistant to help her with her paperwork. She chose Angie, who had scored very high on all the office skills tests, was good with computers, and seemed very self-assured. At first, Angie was very prompt. Soon, however, she occasionally came to work twenty minutes late. In time, she was tardy more frequently. She also began to spend quite a bit of time on personal phone calls, and she began to neglect her work. Gretchen was very frustrated, but she didn't take the initiative to tell Angie her expectations—beating herself up instead because she felt that she wasn't a good boss.

The root of Gretchen's problem was her low self-worth. She was the boss, her expectations of Angie were valid, and she had the legal and ethical right to reprimand Angie for her inappropriate behavior, but she didn't do anything about it. She let her negative feelings build and merely wished the problem would correct itself. Eventually, though, after a long conversation with one of her friends, who instructed her on how to confront Angie in a friendly yet firm way and encouraged her to follow through,

---

*A pseudonym.

Gretchen did speak with Angie about her concerns. Although the conversation took care of the problem, it didn't solve the matter of Gretchen's low self-esteem. That continued until she got professional help.

Inadequate self-esteem degrades relationships, academic performance, and occupational functioning. It also puts us through the psychological discomfort of constantly doubting ourselves. That's one extreme. The other extreme, artificially inflated self-esteem, seriously hurts social interactions and is deemed immoral by the Bible. Adequate self-esteem—a fair and accurate analysis of our qualities and attributes—brings reasonable balance to our behavior.

Some people are more predisposed to having adequate self-esteem than are others, but a large proportion of the self-esteem we have comes from outside influences. In fact, self-esteem is one of our most malleable characteristics.

When I was a psychology student, someone did a study that probably wouldn't be approved by university ethics boards today. It was done to ascertain the effect of verbal statements on self-esteem. This study observed sets of two young people. One in each set was a member of the research team—a "confederate." The other, a voluntary participant, was a student who was being paid a small amount of money to participate in the experiment but didn't know what it involved.

The voluntary participant was asked to take some "psychological tests"—actually, self-esteem tests—and the confederate pretended to be there for the same purpose. As they sat in the waiting room before taking the test, the confederate would either praise the other participant or make cynical remarks and disdaining comments directed at the other student and his or her ideas. The researchers found that the manipulations of the confederate definitely influenced the results that the voluntary participant attained on the self-esteem test.

Everybody has felt inferior at times and rather euphoric about themselves at other times, depending on whether they've been scolded or praised. This is how people build other people up or tear them down—sometimes unknowingly, and other times intentionally. Aware of how powerful our statements about each other are, Paul admonished, "Do not let any unwholesome talk come out of your mouths, but only what is *helpful for building others up according to their needs*, that it may benefit those who listen" (Ephesians 4:29; emphasis added). Notice that this text assumes that there are people—perhaps the naturally insecure—who need a bit more praise than others do. Unlike the color of our eyes, how we feel about ourselves keeps changing as we experience differing internal and external events and processes. Let's examine the various ways people's self-esteem is fed.

What influences our self-esteem

Early life experiences. It is widely believed that the core of a person's self-esteem is shaped during the preschool and school years. Children of that age don't know much about themselves, and they're very eager to observe their own qualities, to compare themselves with others, and to hear what people say about them. Parents, teachers, friends, and neighbors have a lot to do with the shaping of youngsters' self-esteem. Remarks such as "You always keep your room tidy!" or "You're too slow, and you'll always be!" have their effect. When our children are this age, we have to decide whether we want them to possess an adequate concept of themselves, and also what we want them to consider valuable.

A variety of studies conducted with school-aged children show that the characteristics that feed their self-esteem are, first, looks; second, social acceptance/popularity; third, achievement in school; fourth, conduct; and fifth, competency in sports and games. Isn't it interesting that it's how physically attractive we are that has the most influence? We have little control of our appearance, yet if someone is naturally attractive, he or she is likely to receive more praise and end up with greater self-esteem than someone who has not been graced with such pleasing features. Note also that the list contains only one character trait, conduct, and it's next to last on the list. Traits like compassion for others and love for Jesus bring no apparent reward! Here lies the difference between what God understands as valid self-esteem and what the world understands it to be.

The media. As people look at TV shows, movies, the Internet, and billboards, they see what society values. Appearance is at the forefront. Male and female models, advertisers, and famous people determine what society values most—and leave it up to us to reach that standard if we can. Those who attain it are considered successful, and those who don't are considered losers.

Money almost always makes it into the package of what determines worth too. Through enabling people to buy designer clothes, expensive cars and homes, and sophisticated work environments, money brings the respect of the crowd.

The media also exalts power. Whether it's a movie character who is highly regarded and thus influential or a scientist who's so respected that everyone must accept whatever he or she says, individuals who hold power are highly admired. It is unfortunate that many people think of themselves as failures because they're not the powerful people these others are—or purport to be.

Messages from other people. Some have called the people who surround us the mirror of our self-esteem. What these people say to us and about us and how they say it adds to or subtracts from our self-esteem. But we have influence, too, and most of us don't understand how much influence we exert on the self-concepts of our family members, friends, and acquaintances when we comment about them and what they do.

I remember clearly a visit I paid to a middle-aged couple in Madrid, Spain, near where my mother lived. I had just returned from the United States with a doctoral degree in educational psychology, and I had my first professional job. The connection came because the lady had recently become a Seventh-day Adventist and my mother had befriended her at church.

This woman's husband wasn't interested in religion. As soon as we had chatted enough to get past the initial greetings, he said to me, "So, how much money do you make at your new job?"

I must pause to say that as brutal as this inquiry from a mere acquaintance may seem, such questions are quite common in the culture of Spain, especially if an older person does the asking. There it's also appropriate to answer, so I did, telling him what my salary was.

"Well," he replied in a patronizing tone, "I can't believe you went to America to get a graduate degree and you are only earning that!"

It was obvious that, all questions of rudeness aside, his value system was very different from mine. I tried to explain that while I knew that money was necessary, I didn't consider it the most important thing, and that I regarded service, satisfaction, and personal development as important rewards for the work I was doing. Judging by the expression on his face, I knew that he didn't understand my values. He soon left our conversation and occupied himself with his routines around the house.

Though I had little respect for the man, his question did shake me. I felt somehow inadequate because I wasn't making more money. He had dented my self-concept. But then he was an antique dealer whose motto, life philosophy, and guiding principle were one and the same: "Buy low and sell high." What else could he value other than money? Yet, he had hurt my self-esteem. It's a good thing that the feeling left me in a day or two, because I would have had a hard time finding a high-paying job in my profession!

Personal achievement. This is another area intimately related to the development and maintenance of self-esteem. The more we accomplish and the more valuable we consider our achievements to be, the greater is the self-esteem we feel. Again, this isn't an objective measure; it's a strictly personal assessment. I have come across young men and women who were receiving excellent grades, doing quality work, and performing beautiful music but considered themselves inferior. They didn't appreciate what they had. Some of them had this skewed view because some deeply rooted problem from the past prevented them from considering themselves valuable. Others viewed themselves as lacking simply because they wanted the gifts that others had instead of those that were theirs. In any case, they could gain a better perspective on themselves only through much affirmation and much prayer.

In God's image

The Bible presents different measures for our worth and different values for our self-esteem. A quick look at the book of Proverbs reveals that God doesn't attach worth to our attractiveness, possessions, or achievements. Instead, that book associates our worth with qualities such as wisdom, obedience to God, purity, diligence, righteousness, concern for others, honesty, benevolence, joy, temperance, humbleness, integrity, fairness, and so on. These are what the Bible considers to be the attributes that should constitute the source of self-esteem.

The origin of our species should make clear our worth. Scripture says, "God created man in his own image, in the image of God he created him; male and female he created them" (Genesis 1:27). Human beings were made in the Creator's image and in His likeness. They were created as highly intelligent beings who had perfect bodies and were endowed with spiritual powers and the ability to continue to develop. It is true that the onset of sin truncated the endless possibilities that had once been ours, but it is also true that the Creator's imprint, albeit limited now, is still present within us.

We can see this even today. In the midst our evil world, we find compassionate people who are moved to help others despite its costing them significant loss—people who rejoice with those who are rejoicing and who suffer with those who are suffering; people who love good and hate sin and all its consequences. What is the root of these behaviors in human beings who are bent by sin? Apparently, we still bear enough of the image of God that we feel the urge to do godly deeds. This is one of the most puzzling thoughts to the evolutionist. Why should anyone display altruistic behavior toward someone unknown without the hope of receiving anything in return? This doesn't fit the idea of the survival of the fittest, but it makes a lot of sense in the context of a loving Creator who originally passed on His goodness and His character to His creatures, in whom some of these traits still remain.

In addition to being created in the likeness of their Creator, human beings were granted authority to rule over all the earth—to administer its resources wisely in order to bring happiness to the human family. This is another privilege that should enhance our self-esteem—the trust that God has bestowed upon each of us to manage the earth. Unfortunately, we haven't done that very well, but we need to remember that we still possess the power and authority God gave us. Both are excellent sources of self-esteem.

We do have a divine origin. We are made in the image of the God of the universe. Although sin has damaged us and marred the original image, we still bear God's imprint. And, as if this weren't enough, our Creator considers us deserving of salvation and as having the potential to grow throughout eternity. These are infinitely better grounds for self-esteem than those that society holds up for us.

What we see in ourselves

People often have faulty views of themselves. We don't assess our strengths and weaknesses accurately, and this tends to cause trouble. Our dog, Beni, often miscalculated his size. Though he was a small dog, he tended to believe that he was very big, especially under certain conditions—namely, when a member of our family was nearby and Beni saw a big dog running loose. Beni would approach the big dog, stand up on his back legs, place his front legs on either side of the big dog's head, and then, almost nose to nose, he would growl. Big dogs tend to be noble and forgiving, so most of them ignored Beni. But one attacked him and left a scar on his shoulder.

The Bible tells us of individuals who didn't assess their gifts correctly. Take the case of Moses. He was well trained and seasoned, and, above all, he had the Lord backing him. Yet, he still had serious doubts about himself. He begged God not to send him to Pharaoh but to find someone else instead because he wasn't eloquent. " 'Who am I, that I should go to Pharaoh?' " (Exodus 3:11; see also 4:10). Conversely, Jesus had to warn His followers that their self-perception was also mistaken—but in a different way. " 'How can you say to your brother, "Brother, let me take the speck out of your eye," when you yourself fail to see the plank in your own eye?' " (Luke 6:42).

So, while some can't see the bad in themselves, others—like Moses—can't see the good in themselves. But it's there. When Jesus summarized the law, He said the second great commandment was that we should love our neighbors as we love ourselves (see Matthew 22:39), which implies that we should direct a reasonable amount of love toward ourselves. We should feel satisfaction for a job well done and for whatever good there is in us, acknowledging all the while the One who is the Source of all good. This is a very critical point: it was Satan's refusal to acknowledge this Source that set him on the wrong path.

As we judge our skills and abilities, traits, character, appearance, and so on, we are likely to be mistaken in some things. This entails serious risks of our reaching one extreme or the other: we may not be willing to face the challenges God allows to come to us because we have little self-confidence—or because we are so arrogant that God won't bestow His blessings upon us because it might push us further in that direction. To prevent both of these extremes, we must be in constant communion with God, maintaining continually a prayerful attitude.

What others see

When Samuel went to Jesse's house to anoint the new king of Israel, Eliab's height and appearance immediately caught his attention. Based on the young man's looks, Samuel concluded that he was the one God had chosen to be the next king (1 Samuel 16:6). Outward appearance makes us form a strong preliminary judgment about the person before us.

Samuel was a great prophet, an impeccable judge, full of integrity, and with more influence on the people than King Saul. His record of faithfulness stretched all the way back to the beginning of his life. But this didn't prevent him from using the world's criteria in this instance. He did so, and he was mistaken. Ellen White tells us, "Eliab did not fear the Lord. Had he been called to the throne, he would have been a proud, exacting ruler."[1]

If God-chosen individuals can make mistakes in judging others, ordinary people are bound to make great mistakes. That is why Scripture repeatedly discourages us from judging others. Paul reminds us that through faith in Christ Jesus, all the children of God are to learn that "there is neither Jew nor Greek, slave nor free, male nor female" (Galatians 3:28). Here God specifically forbids prejudice—which has been an innate reaction of all human beings throughout time. Prejudice can devastate people's self-esteem. Making preconceived judgments doesn't give people a fair chance to prove themselves.

Self-Esteem

My family and I have lived and worked in four different countries on three continents. Despite spending a considerable amount of time in all those places, we have never been victims of prejudice—with one small exception. As soon as we arrived in one country, we bought a car and quickly applied for insurance. We left all the necessary documentation with an insurance broker, including copies of our driver's licenses and passports. The next day we received a call from the insurance broker informing us that our application for insurance had been denied. Then he asked if by chance my wife had a Spanish passport like I did. When we inquired further, he explained that it was company policy not to insure Americans because they were likely to litigate if they didn't like a settlement.

What God sees

God's regard for His children is based on different values than those that society considers important. Society pushes people to consider themselves worthless if they're poor or uneducated or part of the wrong ethnic group or religious minority, or if they've gone through some tragic event or been a victim of abuse. Chapter 15 of the Gospel of Luke is a jewel that reveals what—or whom—God values. It presents three stories—the lost sheep, the lost coin, and the lost son—that have a common theme: God's concern for the odd, the disadvantaged, the outcast, the sinner, the inferior. Anyone who feels left out because of societal expectations should remember that those whom the world regards as inferior can enjoy the special, intimate care of God and His angels. In these three stories, the protagonists—the shepherd, the woman, and the father—cared more for the lost than for those in positions of advantage. And when the lost are found, the whole universe rejoices.

God sees tremendous potential in each and every one of His creatures—*in all of us*. He doesn't leave us to struggle alone but offers to lead, to guide, and to help: "I will counsel you and watch over you" (Psalm 32:8). He cares so much for us that He yearns to care for us as "the apple of your [His] eye" (Psalm 17:8).

A new self

The apostle Paul urges his readers to "put on the new self" (Ephesians 4:24). People have different opinions of what constitutes a new self. Recently, I was approaching Los Angeles in my car, headed west on my way to Woodland Hills for a reunion with former students. Not knowing the area, I entered the destination into my global positioning system (GPS) and then chose the shortest route. The GPS took me off the interstate highway and onto Ventura Boulevard. This route was slow but very interesting. As I drove, I could observe the people who were walking along the street and the various shops and businesses along the way. This gave me a glimpse into the services that people in that area patronized. It seemed to me that there were an unusually high number of hair salons, clothing shops, aesthetic dentistry and plastic surgery practices, specialty decoration shops, and imported-car dealerships. I concluded that the people living around Hollywood had to care more for their appearance and the impression they make than the rest of us do.

In contrast, the new self that Paul wrote about is the product of a godly method of building self-esteem. According to the criteria outlined in Scripture, *things* don't make us more beautiful. Instead, *character* is the key to true beauty and self-worth. Ephesians 4:25–32 lists the activities God considers important. He wants us

- to be honest and truthful to the people around us;
- to keep our tempers under control, and if we do become angry, to seek to resolve things quickly;
- to work hard to have enough so that we can share with those in need;
- to build others up through what we say;
- to avoid grieving the Holy Spirit;
- to get rid of bitterness, brawling, slandering, and all kinds of bad traits;
- and to be kind, compassionate, and forgiving.

Both God and spiritually wise men and women consider all of these actions and qualities to have true value.

If you have problems with self-esteem, reflect on your origin: you're created in the image of God! And ponder your destiny: you're saved by grace! Then fervently ask God to give you wisdom to "think of yourself with sober judgment, in accordance with the measure of faith God has given you" (Romans 12:3).

---

1. Ellen G. White, *Patriarchs and Prophets,* 638.

CHAPTER 10

Jealousy

Sybil Hart and Heather Carrington, from the Department of Human Development and Family Studies at Texas Tech University, wanted to find out whether six-month-old babies experienced jealousy.[1] Thirty-two first-time mothers agreed to participate in the study with their babies.

The researchers made two two-minute-long video recordings of each pair, using two cameras: one focused on the mother and the other on the baby. The baby would watch his or her mother hold a baby doll, talk to it pleasantly, and stroke its belly, and then the baby would see his or her mother read a book aloud, again using pleasant tones. The researchers recorded and rated the emotions the babies displayed. While the babies spent most of the time gazing at their mothers, they displayed significantly more negative responses when they saw their mothers interact with the doll than when she read the book. This indicates that jealousy is a genetic trait that appears at a very early stage of development.

Not only does jealousy appear very early in life, but it also stretches back to the most remote past of our collective history. It is considered the first sin, having come into existence even before humankind was created. It has existed ever since, and it will continue to exist until Jesus comes and transforms the redeemed.

Jealousy is a great enemy of positive interpersonal interactions. It may become so acute that it distorts perception. It's the opposite of love and altruism—the jealous person considering the person who is the focus of their jealousy as an object that stands in the way of their happiness. They reason, *This person's presence (or possessions, etc.) are keeping me from being happy, and I will do whatever it takes to replace or become like him/her (or to have his/her possessions, etc.).* Jealousy is a very disturbing emotion that brings extreme discomfort to those suffering from it, and it may eventually motivate psychological manipulation (false accusations and/or backbiting) or aggression (verbal abuse, physical battering, or even attempts to kill).

In this chapter we'll look at a series of Bible characters who were jealous of what someone else was or had. We'll see that this emotion brings awful complications. We'll witness the victory of the envied person in one form or another and note that the result was always disastrous for the jealous individual, who had to witness the success and triumph of the object of his or her jealousy. The Lord has preserved these scriptural accounts and advice to warn us to avoid the path of envy and jealousy. He invites us instead to love our neighbors and to rejoice with them in their gifts, achievements, and possessions.

Satan

Although written as oracles against Babylon, Isaiah 14 and Ezekiel 28 use language that better fits the rebellious angel Lucifer rather than it does human beings. Isaiah describes the cause of Lucifer's expulsion from heaven. In his heart, Satan said, " 'I will make myself like the Most High' " (Isaiah 14:14). But instead of raising his throne to the level of God's throne, he was "cast down to the earth," "brought down to the grave, to the depths of the pit" (verses 12, 15). In this passage and Ezekiel 28, Lucifer is described as the "morning star," the "son of the dawn," the "model of perfection," "full of wisdom," "perfect in beauty," "anointed as a guardian cherub," and "blameless." All these qualities began to change when he allowed jealousy to grow within him.

According to Ellen White, when the Father said to Jesus, "Let us make man in our image," the plan to create humankind made Satan jealous of Jesus because he wanted to be a member of the Deity. He chose to contemplate what Christ had rather than being satisfied with the gifts that were his. His desire to be like God and not to submit to the authority of Jesus led him to rebel. Then he campaigned among the angels to get as many as he could to support his cause. "All the heavenly host were summoned to appear before the Father to have each case decided. It was there determined that Satan should be expelled from heaven, with all the angels who had joined him in the rebellion. Then there was war in heaven. Angels were engaged in the battle; Satan wished to conquer the Son of God and those who were submissive to His will. But the good and true angels prevailed, and Satan, with his followers, was driven from heaven."[2]

Satan's next step was to infect the beings created in God's image with this toxic element. It was Satan himself who tempted the first human beings with the jealous ambition that had motivated his rebellion. When you eat of this tree, he promised, " *'You will be like God'* " (Genesis 3:5; emphasis added). Eve fell to the temptation, Adam followed, and ever since then, sin has spread like an epidemic, causing the terrible consequences that are visible through all of our world's history, including today.

Jealous ambition is one of the favorite modes of temptation that Satan and his demons use. A fable says that when the devil was traveling across the desert of Libya, he noticed a group of demons who were trying to tempt a hermit. They presented seductions of the flesh, doubts about God's Word, and fear about the future, but they couldn't get the hermit to sin in deed or in thought. The devil stepped forward and said, "Your methods are too crude. Permit me one moment." Then, going to the hermit, he said, "Have you heard the news? Your brother has been made the bishop of Alexandria." According to the fable, a scowl of malignant jealousy immediately clouded the face of the holy man.[3]

James put it in this way: "Where you have envy [jealousy] and selfish ambition, there you find disorder and *every* evil practice. But the wisdom that comes from heaven is first of all pure; then peace-loving, considerate, submissive, full of mercy and good fruit, impartial and sincere" (James 3:16, 17; emphasis added). This is excellent news! In the same way that jealousy and selfish ambition cause disorder and all kinds of evil practices, the knowledge of God through Jesus Christ causes all kinds of love-based deeds.

Joseph's brothers

In the speech Stephen made just before he was stoned to death, he identified the motivation behind the cruel behavior of Joseph's brothers: " 'Because the patriarchs were jealous of Joseph, they sold him as a slave into Egypt' " (Acts 7:9). It's hard to believe that the sons of Jacob could sell their brother as a slave to foreign traders, even considering his dreams and their father's favoritism. But jealousy is viciously powerful. "Jealousy is cruel as the grave: the coals thereof are coals of fire, which hath a most vehement flame" (Song of Solomon 8:6, KJV).

Jealousy follows a crazy spiral path. It starts with the desire to build ourselves up by degrading our neighbor. If that works, we're not left with a sense of accomplishment, but rather with bitter remorse. If it doesn't work, we feel insecure, inadequate, and humiliated. These feelings bring about greater jealousy, which creates within us an even stronger desire to build ourselves up by degrading our neighbor, returning us to step one but with greater intensity.

When spun often and deeply enough, this process means death. It's why Cain killed Abel, Haman wanted to kill Mordecai, the princes of Babylon attempted to kill Daniel, Herod killed scores of innocent infants, and so on.

Joseph welcomed his brothers to Egypt, forgave them, and blessed them, but the fear sown by their deed of jealousy stayed alive for at least seventeen years beyond their reconciliation. When Jacob died, the brothers reasoned, " 'What if Joseph holds a grudge against us and pays us back for all the wrongs we did to him?' " (Genesis 50:15). But Joseph knew that the right thing for him to do was to forgive his brothers and leave the consequences with God. So, he tried to reassure them. " 'Don't be afraid,' " he said. " 'Am I in the place of God?' " (verse 19).

Saul

David first entered the service of King Saul when some of the king's attendants recommended him, reporting that he had suitable qualifications: he played the harp, was a brave warrior, was well spoken and handsome, and the Lord was with him. Saul sent for David, and Scripture says that he "liked him very much, and David became one of his armor-bearers" (1 Samuel 16:21). Saul was also very supportive when David offered to fight Goliath. He even offered David the use of his armor and sent him off with a blessing. After the victory, Saul realized the benefits that came to him from having David permanently in his house, and he didn't let him go home. After David carried out a number of missions successfully, Saul gave him a high rank in the army, which met with everyone's approval.

But things took a 180-degree turn when Saul and his men were returning home from a battle against the Philistines. They heard a group of women playing musical instruments and dancing to this song: " 'Saul has slain his thousands, and David his tens of thousands' " (1 Samuel 18:7). The refrain angered Saul, "and from that time on Saul kept a jealous eye on David" (verse 9). The epigram fits, "[The envious] praise only that which they can surpass but that which surpasses them—they censure."[4]

Jealousy

When Saul began to keep a jealous eye on David, his mental health and moral behavior deteriorated. The following sequence of events reveals his unfortunate path.

- On the day after Saul heard the women sing, he hurled his spear at David twice while David was playing the harp for him (18:10, 11).
- Saul became afraid of David. Perhaps he feared losing his kingly position or that David would become the hero of the nation. Above all, he was afraid "because the LORD was with David but had left Saul" (18:12).
- Saul offered his daughter Michal in marriage to David, hoping that she would become a snare to him and the Philistines would kill him (18:21).
- Saul ordered his son Jonathan and all the attendants to kill David (19:1), but they, being aware of Saul's blind obsession, didn't follow his orders.
- Although Saul seemed convinced by Jonathan of how preposterous his intentions were, he soon tried again to pin David to the wall with his spear (19:4–6, 10).
- He sent his men to David's home to kill him, but Michal succeeded in alerting David and helping him flee (19:11–16).
- Saul sent his men to Naioth at Ramah, where David had found refuge with Samuel, to capture him. They didn't succeed because the Spirit of God took possession of them (19:19–21).
- Saul himself went to Naioth, and the Spirit of God prevented him from taking any action (19:23, 24).
- Saul insulted his own son Jonathan for remaining loyal to David and ordered him to bring David to him, "for he must die!" (20:30, 31).
- He had Ahitub and Ahitub's son Ahimelech, priests of the Lord in Nob, killed because they had shown kindness to David. He also killed the remaining priests of Nob, a total of eighty-five, and the entire population of that town, including "men and women, its children and infants, and its cattle, donkeys and sheep" (22:11–19).
- Day after day Saul searched for David, who kept moving from place to place, "but God did not give David into his hands" (23:14).

- Saul made an alliance with his enemies, the Ziphites, to help him track David down (23:19–23).
- Saul and David had an emotionally moving encounter after David spared the king's life, but soon Saul was on his way to the Desert of Ziph with three thousand men, searching for David again (24:8–22; 26:2).
- Saul and David had a second positive encounter after David again refused to take Saul's life when he could easily have done so. This time Saul admitted his sin, promised not to try to harm David again, and blessed him (26:17–25). He did stop persecuting David, but then he headed down the road that ended in his destruction.
- Terrified by the Philistines' attack, Saul chose to consult a witch. She invoked an evil spirit that appeared in the form of Samuel, who was dead. Saul prostrated himself before this evil spirit, which then predicted that Israel would be defeated and Saul and his sons killed all on the same day (chapter 28).
- When the Philistines attacked and were defeating the Israelites, Saul killed himself, "and his three sons and his armor-bearer and all his men died together that same day" (31:6).

What a sad ending! As in many other cases, in this story jealousy was the first step that led downhill into many other forms of evil and even death! It is true that God intended David to have the throne regardless of the circumstances. But, like any other situation involving good and evil, the people could choose on which side they would stand. Saul had many opportunities to change the course of events, but he persistently made the wrong choices. Jonathan's course contrasted strongly with that of his father. Jonathan positioned himself on the side of righteousness, avoiding jealousy and disregarding the claim to the throne that he could have made. Because he understood how absurd his father's behavior was, he protected David's life at the risk of his own. Yet, he stood firm "at his father's side through the dark days of his declining power, and at his side falling at the last—the name of Jonathan is treasured in heaven, and it stands on earth a witness to the existence and the power of unselfish love."[5]

The chief priests

The men who ruled Judaism in the first century were also touched by jealousy of Jesus and the first Christian leaders. The consequences were painful to all. Even Pilate, who wasn't a member of the religious community, realized that the rulers had handed Jesus to him because of envy (Matthew 27:18; Mark 15:10). Their jealousy had grown throughout the Savior's ministry to the point where they would do anything to kill Him. They also became jealous of Jesus' followers—specifically, of Peter, Paul, and Barnabas—and they sought their death. Their emotions demonstrated the truth of the proverb that says, "Those who are green with envy often become red with anger."

Peter and the other apostles were causing a great commotion in Jerusalem. Crowds from the city and from surrounding towns were coming to hear about salvation through Jesus. They brought their sick and demon-possessed to the apostles, and they were healed. The Jewish people were beginning to recognize that God was working powerfully through the apostles. "Then the high priest and . . . the Sadducees, were filled with jealousy. They arrested the apostles and put them in the public jail" (Acts 5:17, 18).

Paul and Barnabas were in Antioch of Pisidia. Paul preached in the synagogue on several Sabbaths, and some of the Jews and their Gentile converts became very interested in what he and Barnabas were saying. One Sabbath, almost the whole city congregated to hear them speak. Luke reports, however, that "*when the Jews saw the crowds,* they were filled with jealousy and talked abusively against what Paul was saying" (Acts 13:45; emphasis added). Later on, they collaborated with prominent women and men in the city to stir up persecution, and they managed to expel the apostles from the region.

It appears that when crowds of the common people became interested enough in the apostles to follow them around, the chief priests became jealous. As we saw earlier, that was true also of Saul when he heard a group of women acclaiming David's victories. Crowds have an amazing power upon people's emotions and behaviors. They can transform people.

When I came of age, I had to serve in the armed forces of Spain. At the time, that was required of all Spanish young men. Being a Seventh-day Adventist, I chose the alternative of serving with the Red Cross—a longer but more attractive alternative for conscientious objectors. We were assigned various kinds of duties, such as assisting with ambulances when there had been an accident and attending large public gatherings in case stretcher bearers were needed to transport injured people.

One of the assignments considered most desirable was that of working at the soccer games that took place every Sunday during the nine-month-long premier league season. I wasn't very fond of soccer, but I was happy to go to those events, which each attracted a hundred thousand spectators. My interest in human behavior often drew my eyes away from the field and to the crowds. I witnessed all kinds of emotions and behaviors among the spectators: groups of hooligans screaming at the top of their voices, verbal and physical fights between fans of rival teams, people jumping and throwing objects, and profoundly sad faces when the local team lost. I wondered how a fan would behave if he or she watched a match alone, without the presence of the crowd.

One day, while those of us who had been assigned to serve at a particular game waited for the stadium to empty—a process that took between thirty and forty-five minutes—we noticed one spectator asleep at the end of his row up in the highest tier of seats. The Red Cross men nearby went to wake him up and tell him the match was over. When they reached him, they found that he was dead. He had died of a heart attack. We wanted to find out whether he had died of sorrow or elation, but we never learned which team he was cheering for. We thought it very shocking that hundreds of persons had walked by this man without noticing that he was dead.

Why were the chief priests, elders, Pharisees, and others jealous of Jesus and, later on, of His disciples?

- They had a lot of authority, but the common people had little respect for them. Jesus, however, had the people's respect because of His example, His love for people, and how He spoke.
- The Jewish leaders' love of approbation repelled the multitudes, while the humble sincerity of Jesus and the apostles drew large crowds.
- The religious leaders couldn't perform miracles in the name of God, but Jesus and the apostles gave constant evidence that the Omnipotent's supernatural powers worked through them.
- Although the chief priests knew the law perfectly, they used their knowledge of it to benefit themselves, whereas Jesus offered a loving interpretation of the law.
- Jesus often asked them questions they couldn't—or didn't want to—answer.
- They sought the praise of the common people by making sure that the people saw them praying in the synagogue and in other public places. Jesus didn't "put on" religiosity.

- They saw Jesus' superiority and feared that He would become the king of the Jews, holding the power they craved.
- Even though they often managed to deceive the people with their pious pretensions, they couldn't deceive Jesus.

Jealousy and envy increase proportionally as others experience success. That's a diabolic tendency of human nature. Depending on one's culture, personal characteristics, and principles, it may be more or less pronounced, but the seed is universal.

Paul has set before us the highly desirable goal of rejoicing at the strength and growth of our neighbors. This is how we defeat envy and jealousy. In his final remarks to the Corinthian church, Paul exemplified this attitude, writing, "We are glad whenever we are weak but you are strong; and our prayer is for your perfection." He reminded his readers that God had given him authority "for building you up, not for tearing you down" (2 Corinthians 13:9, 10).

The Bible shows jealousy to be one of the worst possible emotions human beings can experience. "Anger is cruel and fury overwhelming, but who can stand before jealousy?" (Proverbs 27:4). This emotion is found at the very root of evil. It causes all sorts of disasters. If you are tempted by jealousy, envy, or covetousness, the only solution is the love of Jesus. It enables us to love one another as Jesus loves us. "Keep yourselves in the love of God, looking for the mercy of our Lord Jesus Christ unto eternal life" (Jude 21, KJV).

---

1. Sybil Hart and Heather Carrington, "Jealousy in 6-Month-Old Infants," *Infancy* 3 (2002): 395–402.

2. Ellen G. White, *Early Writings* (Washington, D.C.: Review and Herald®, 1945), 146.

3. Paul Lee Tan, *Encyclopedia of 15,000 Illustrations,* entry 6002.

4. Charles Caleb Colton, *Lacon; or Many Things in Few Words,* revised ed. (New York: William Gowans, 1849), 270.

5. Ellen G. White, *Education* (Mountain View, Calif.: Pacific Press®, 1952), 157.

CHAPTER 11

Addictions

The weather that day in Bracknell, Berkshire, England, allowed me to sit on a public bench along one of the streets while I ate my lunch. I soon discovered that the bench where I was sitting was in front of an establishment filled with electronic games. As I munched my sandwich, I could see a slot machine near the entrance. I watched as a man in his twenties began to put in coins—half-pound, one-pound, and two-pound coins, not just small change. Suddenly, the sounds of bells and whistles filled the air, and lots of coins poured out of the machine. I thought the man had gotten what he wanted, but instead of leaving with the loot, he put the coins back into the machine one by one, as if the machine had lost them and he was returning them. Of course, the one-armed bandit accepted every single piece of precious metal. The man checked all his pockets to confirm that he had no more coins, and then he left. I don't know whether he was hooked on gambling. If so, he would no doubt return the next day with a new bag of coins to repeat the scene.

Why this illogical behavior? The young man probably wanted to win the jackpot. But even if he were to win it, he'd already have put in more money than it would have paid him.

Addictions of any kind form serious barriers to freedom. When they control people's behavior, the people have lost their freedom. No wonder happiness has been defined as freedom from addictions.

The best known addictions are the chemical ones—addictions to drugs such as marijuana, cocaine, and heroin; and to other substances, such as alcohol, tobacco, caffeine, sleeping pills, and painkillers that are considered acceptable because they have been legalized and regulated. All of those substances, to a greater or lesser extent, cause the following:

- *Dependence.* This means that when people have taken the substance a few times, they find it difficult to stop using it. This is partly because of habit and partly because of chemical processes that make them feel uncomfortable until they take the substance again.
- *Withdrawal.* This refers to the severe symptoms people experience when they quit using a substance.
- *Reinforcement.* This is the psychological mechanism created when people experience a reward or a feeling of pleasure from an activity or substance, which inclines them to use it again and again.
- *Tolerance.* This results from the body's adaptation to a substance, which necessitates increasing the dose to obtain the same level of results that the addict has previously experienced.
- *Intoxication.* This is the dulling of sensory and mental faculties by a substance.

These responses explain why people have such difficulty giving up addictive substances. More often than not, they have to have the support of their families, close friends, therapeutic groups, and professionals. And above all, they need the strength God will give them.

The overwhelming majority of Seventh-day Adventists around the world are free from the substances I've listed above. However, there are many nonchemical habits that can become powerful addictions: sex, pornography, gambling, risky investments, the accumulation of money or goods, video gaming, texting, and care for one's image. Furthermore, people abuse and become addicted to common necessities such as food, medicine, shopping, and exercise. Legal or illicit, chemical or nonchemical, socially approved or rejected, health hazard or innocuous, all addictions limit freedom, and some take it away completely. It is immoral for those who understand that they are created in God's image and created free (Genesis 1:27; 2:16) to make decisions that might cause them to become enslaved by a chemical or a habit.

Chemical addictions

There are many substances that can produce addiction. Stimulants—

such as cocaine, amphetamines, nicotine, and caffeine—provide extra motivation and energy. Depressants—such as barbiturates, benzodiazepines, alcohol, and opiates, including heroin—can calm people or cheer up a depressive mood. Hallucinogens—such as LSD, marijuana, and hashish—produce hallucinations, marked changes of perception that sometimes are pleasant, sometimes horrific. Inhalants—such as glue, toluene, and ether—sometimes act as depressants and sometimes as hallucinogens. Steroids—such as doping agents and bodybuilders—cause a growth in muscular mass that enables people to increase their strength and improve their physical performance. Let's look at a few addictions, beginning with the drug that poses the most problems.

Alcohol. Of all addictive substances, alcohol and tobacco place the greatest burdens upon health, societies, economies, families, communities, and nations. According to the World Health Organization, there are 2 billion alcohol users and 1.3 billion smokers. Contrast those numbers with the mere 185 million users of all illicit drugs combined.[1]

Alcohol is the chief culprit among chemical addictions, affecting the greatest number of people. Complicating matters, it has an attractive image: wineries are delightful places to visit, wine is used for toasting people during special occasions and celebrations, alcoholic drinks are associated with intellectual activities, and they are a favorite among the upper middle classes. In addition, there is now some evidence that when used in moderation, alcohol may reduce the risk of heart disease and diabetes.

Is this the last word? Probably not, if the history of tobacco is any indication. Just a few generations ago, science said that smoking was good for one's health. For decades, Clark Gable, Humphrey Bogart, and other Hollywood stars were made to look more attractive with ever-present cigarettes. Nowadays, tobacco is associated with terrible health hazards and has been discredited—it thrives primarily among the working classes and in developing countries.

The Bible strongly warns us about alcohol, showing not only its attractive face, but also its ugly side:

> Do not gaze at wine when it is red,
>> when it sparkles in the cup,
>> when it goes down smoothly!
> In the end it bites like a snake
>> and poisons like a viper (Proverbs 23:31, 32).

Addictions

The same chapter names a few consequences of alcohol consumption: woe, sorrow, strife, complaints, needless bruises, bloodshot eyes, strange sights, and wild imaginings. It closes with a reminder of the mentality addiction produces, " 'When will I wake up so I can find another drink?' " (verse 35).

Consumption of alcohol has long-term effects: malnutrition, cirrhosis of the liver, peripheral nerve damage, cardiac disorders, pancreatitis, gastritis, gastroduodenal ulcers, Wernicke-Korsakoff syndrome, early mortality, and, in the case of pregnant women, premature birth, fetal alcohol syndrome, and certain congenital abnormalities. There are also behavioral and emotional complications. For example, Janet C. Greenblatt, from the Substance Abuse and Mental Health Services Administration, examined data about fifteen- to twenty-year-olds across the United States.[2] Here are some of the results:

- Twenty-one percent of the fifteen- to twenty-year-olds involved in car accidents had been drinking.
- People who begin drinking before fifteen years of age are four times more likely to become alcoholics than are those who start drinking at the age of twenty-one or older.
- College drinkers were 2.3 times more likely than nondrinkers to force sexual touching or sexual intercourse upon an unwilling partner.
- Eighty percent of all high school seniors and dropouts said they had gotten drunk and had driven under the influence.
- Fifty percent of high school seniors and dropouts reported that alcohol caused them to have sickness, absenteeism, and problems with the law.
- Fifty percent of heavy drinkers reported that they had used an illicit drug (marijuana, hallucinogens, and/or inhalants) in the past thirty days.
- Half of the drinkers reported poor school work, compared with 27 percent of nondrinkers.
- In comparison with nondrinkers, those who were drinkers were three times more likely to say that they had tried to hurt or kill themselves.
- Drinkers were three to five times more likely to say they had run away from home.
- Drinkers were three to four times more likely to say that they had stolen or shoplifted.

- Drinkers were two to three times more likely to say that they had destroyed things, threatened people, and/or physically attacked people.
- Heavy drinkers were three times more likely to have been involved in a physical fight.
- Drinkers were twice as likely to have disobeyed school authorities, to have cut classes, and/or to have skipped school.

Some Adventists are ignoring the church's historic position of abstemiousness by drinking "in moderation." That seems a pity when we have been entrusted with a health message that has proven itself for more than one hundred years—one that excluded the use of alcoholic beverages.

I won't be drinking alcohol in moderation. My father was an alcoholic who caused a great deal of pain to our family. He took his life at the age of forty-two, when I was two and my sister was five, leaving us in a most unpleasant situation. I am positive that if my father had been brought up in an Adventist family in his day, he wouldn't have used alcohol, either in moderation or in excess, and his life would have been of much more use. As it was, alcohol caused our family unnecessary suffering. I thank God that my mother embraced the Adventist faith and then lured my sister and me into church when we were teenagers. I have sometimes wondered whether I would be alive if I hadn't continued to follow the abstemiousness I accepted in my youth.

Other chemical addictions. There are other chemicals that may lead to less obvious and destructive addictions; among them, sugar and caffeine. Psychologists from Princeton University have presented evidence of sugar addiction cycles in rats, including steps such as bingeing, withdrawal, and craving.[3] The experience of many people suggests that human beings are subject to becoming addicted to sugar too.

Caffeine, a mild stimulant contained in coffee, tea, and various soft drinks, has been found to cause dependence, tolerance, and withdrawal. In fact, the *Diagnostic and Statistical Manual of Mental Disorder* (DSM-IV) classifies the consumption of 250 mg of caffeine per day as caffeine intoxication. The effects are nervousness, restlessness, insomnia, diuresis, an excess of blood in one's cheeks, muscle twitching, digestive problems, rambling flow of thought and speech, tachycardia, and psychomotor agitation.

Nonchemical addictions
There are addictive practices that are based on behavior and habit rather

than on ingesting physical substances. Although the causes of these addictions may differ, the psychological processes are remarkably similar to those caused by chemical addictions. That's why the original twelve steps of Alcoholics Anonymous work equally well for any of the other group therapies: Gamblers Anonymous, Workaholics Anonymous, Sexaholics Anonymous, Shoplifters Anonymous, Overeaters Anonymous, Smokers Anonymous, and so on. Let's examine a few common non-chemical addictions.

Sex addiction. The Bible presents sexuality as a source of enjoyment for both marriage partners and as a way for them to strengthen their relationship. Solomon, in the context of his warnings against adultery, presents a very clear statement of the benefits of love for husband and wife:

> May your fountain be blessed,
> and may you rejoice in the wife of your youth.
> A loving doe, a graceful deer—
> may her breasts satisfy you always,
> may you ever be captivated by her love (Proverbs 5:18, 19).

This gift from God to humanity was granted not only for procreation but also as a source of joy, closeness, and unity in marriage (Genesis 1:27, 28; 1 Corinthians 7:2).

However, when sex is taken away from its original framework and purpose, it becomes a source of trouble. Adultery produces the following consequences: infidelity to God because it is a transgression of the seventh commandment and dishonors Him (1 Corinthians 6:19, 20); unfaithfulness to the spouse who is wronged; damage to the stability of the marriage; injury to the adulterer, because, as Paul says, "all other sins a man commits are outside his body, but he who sins sexually sins against his own body" (1 Corinthians 6:18); and serious risk of falling into an addiction.

Adultery inclines people to sexual addiction when the sexual interaction is satisfying and no one finds out. The pleasure obtained will draw the adulterer to repeat the behavior, which then may become addictive. When I worked in graduate education, we had to deal with a couple of cases of adultery. The president of the school addressed the masters' and doctoral students—most of whom were married and had children—about this topic and gave a very serious warning: "If you think that you can cheat on your wife and nobody will find out, you are wrong. Satan will make sure to uncover your act, so that you and your church get discredited." He wanted these students to reflect on the consequences before they rushed into an illicit relationship.

Jesus' definition of adultery includes more than the physical act. He said, " 'Anyone who looks at a woman lustfully has already committed adultery with her in his heart' " (Matthew 5:28). That definition has direct implications for contemporary temptations: pornographic magazines and movies, strip bars, and cybersex. The latter, an online erotic/romantic conversation frequently accompanied by masturbation, has grown phenomenally over the past few years. And now, as many women as men are participating. It is estimated that 9 percent of those who try cybersex become addicts. Indicators of addiction include personality changes, demands for privacy, ignoring household chores, lack of interest in sex with one's spouse, lies about credit card charges, and lack of interaction with family members.

The impact of cybersex addiction on marriage and family life is significant. Marital and family therapists as well as divorce lawyers are reporting an increase in the number of couples seeking divorces due to online infidelity. Jennifer P. Schneider is a physician certified in internal medicine, addiction medicine, and pain management who works with the Arizona Community Physicians group. She surveyed a sample of individuals whose spouses were involved in Internet sex. Respondents felt hurt, betrayed, rejected, abandoned, devastated, lonely, ashamed, isolated, humiliated, jealous, and angry, and suffered low self-esteem.[4] In 68 percent of the couples, one or both partners had lost interest in sex with their spouse. This virtual infidelity had begun to take its toll: 22 percent of the respondents were separated or divorced, and several others were thinking about leaving their relationship. Practically all felt that cyberaffairs were as emotionally painful as were live affairs. As far as the children were concerned, they were exposed to cyberporn and neglected by their addictive parent, and many of them had to suffer the consequence of marital conflict and separation as well.

In addition to the profound family problems caused by virtual affairs, those who participate in them suffer consequences to themselves. Andreas Philaretou and his associates examined the effects of cybersex compulsion on those addicted to it.[5] They took a case-study approach based on extensive interviews with male participants addicted to Internet sex. Guilt, depressive symptoms, symptoms of anxiety, and an inability to experience intimacy with real-life partners were some of the consequences of online sex addiction that they observed.

Addictions

We need to avoid taking even one step in the wrong direction. "Keep to a path far from [an adulterer], do not go near the door of her house" (Proverbs 5:8). A youth pastor of my day used to give us good advice. He said, "Imagine that you notice that you like a certain young woman, but you find out that she is married. You have two options: either you discard the idea completely, or you start fantasizing and imagining times and places in which you would be in her company, ignoring the fact that she is married. You better follow the first path while you can easily do so because the second will open the door to trouble." His point was that we should say No before things became too complicated. "Submit yourselves, then, to God. Resist the devil, and he will flee from you" (James 4:7).

Gambling. This activity is one of the pastimes most likely to cause addiction. People start making a few "innocent" bets, and the occasional payoffs make them try again and again in the hope that soon they'll have a big payoff that will compensate for all they've lost. Evidences of addiction include an obsessive preoccupation with gambling, lies, loss of all available money, and then borrowing and even stealing so they can continue to gamble.

Bingo, poker, slot machines, roulette, sports betting, and the lottery are some of the forms of gambling that may lead to addiction. The Bible doesn't speak directly of gambling or betting, but we can obtain its guidance by noting what it says about related matters. For example, it says that those who don't work aren't entitled to eat (2 Thessalonians 3:10). The tenth commandment forbids coveting (Exodus 20:17), which is the emotion gamblers experience when they think of the top prize. And Paul warns against the love of money, which he calls the root of all evil (1 Timothy 6:10). We can infer that gamblers and betters are money lovers, for they wouldn't incur such heavy debts in time, money, and energy just to win a little cash.

I attended all my elementary grades at San Ildefonso School in downtown Madrid. It's the oldest primary school in Spain, and one of the oldest in Europe, having been founded back in the late fifteenth century. Shortly after the National Lottery of Spain was created in 1763, the boys of San Ildefonso were commissioned to draw the winning numbers and to sing of the big prizes at each drawing, a tradition that continues to this day.

For a few years, I helped in the drawing three times a month. We activated the mechanism that extracted the lucky beechwood balls that bore the fire-engraved numbers. All the little balls were contained in a giant, transparent spherical container. As a child, I didn't fully understand the mathematical probability of drawing the right number out of the sixty thousand possible, but I distinctly remember saying to myself, "When I grow up, I won't play lottery—it's so difficult to get a prize!" And I was right!

Today, national lotteries include a million participants—or more. What are the odds of winning a secondary prize, and what are the chances of winning the top prize? The probability is so remote that it doesn't justify investing a single penny. But this logical analysis doesn't convince the many people who patronize these forms of gambling. Why? Not because they're simply greedy or desire to make big money quickly. Self-esteem appears to be a principal factor. Many people find satisfaction in fantasizing about winning because of what they imagine it will do for their egos. When they don't win, they shift their hopes to winning the next time—so they gamble again and again. We can counteract that hope by contrasting the many sure blessings we receive from our God through Jesus Christ with the remote probability of winning the lottery.

Possessions. Wealth, in and of itself, doesn't have to be evil. In fact, Job, a very rich man, was God's favorite man of his generation. The Bible, however, does warn against the *wrong attitude toward money and assets.* For example, as we have noted above, Paul tells his pupil Timothy that "love of money is a root of all kinds of evil," and he explains its danger by saying that some have lost their faith due to such love. And Jesus said, " 'A man's life does not consist in the abundance of his possessions' " (Luke 12:15).

The rich young ruler was a good Jew in faith and practice. But he valued his possessions more than the kingdom of God. That is why, when Jesus asked him to sell them and follow Him, he couldn't bear the pain of losing what he considered most important. Therefore, "the man's face fell" and "he went away sad" (Mark 10:22). His faulty priorities probably cost him eternal life.

People's love of material things becomes especially dangerous when they focus their lives on accumulating them. Some may dedicate a disproportionate amount of time to monitoring their investments, thus neglecting God, relationships, and recreation. The Internet has made it possible for us to navigate from bank account to bank account. We can make all the transfers we want to—even internationally. And we can invest in the stock exchange without leaving our homes. The constant change of indexes and rates may bind us to our computers for endless hours in order to make an extra five or ten dollars. This is a sign of addiction.

We need to honestly and openly ask the Lord for our necessities: "Give me neither poverty nor riches; feed me with food convenient for me: Lest I be full, and deny thee, and say, Who is the LORD? or lest I be poor, and steal, and take the name of my God in vain" (Proverbs 30:8, 9, KJV).

Personal image. Years ago, I had a colleague who commented to me that his wife was having problems with her weight. She would tell him, "Dear, every time I look at myself in the mirror, I get depressed." And he would reply to her, "Then don't look at yourself in the mirror!" He loved her the same with or without those extra ten pounds. He accepted her as she was.

Why did she get depressed? For one thing, society has placed an excessive value on personal image, creating frustration and depression in those who differ from the norm. This creates business. The worldwide cosmetics industry generates returns equivalent to more than half of the global food retail market. In addition to buying cosmetics, many people spend their resources on body building, face lifting, Botox injections, hair transplants, plastic surgery, special diets, and so on, in order to improve their appearance.

The issue here, again, is a matter of one's values. In a recent Travel Channel program, five South Pacific islanders from a primitive culture were brought to America to witness the way Americans live. Among the many things they experienced was a beauty treatment in Southern California. The beautician asked, "Would you like to look ten years younger?" The Pacific Islander she asked, replied, "No, I would prefer to live ten years longer!" In his culture, age—and even looking old—were highly valued. In the beautician's culture, looking young is of supreme value.

The apostle Peter indicated what Christians should value: "Your beauty should not come from outward adornment. . . . Instead, it should be that of your inner self, the unfading beauty of a gentle and quiet spirit, which is of great worth in God's sight" (1 Peter 3:3, 4). It isn't outward beauty that counts but the gentleness of a Christlike character.

There are still other forms of addiction that we haven't discussed—food, exercise, work, TV, video gaming, surfing the Web, text messaging, shopping, pursuing hobbies, even Facebook. Counselors report an increasing number of individuals who say they're having problems with their use of social-networking sites such as Facebook and MySpace. Some spend ninety minutes a day on these sites, searching for newly posted pictures and messages.

If you're at risk of falling into an addiction or if you're suffering under one, consider seriously turning to Jesus for the freedom He can help you find. " 'If the Son sets you free, you will be free indeed' " (John 8:36).

---

1. See www.who.int/substance_abuse/facts/global_burden/en/index.html.

2. Janet C. Greenblatt, "Patterns of Alcohol Use Among Adolescents and Associations with Emotional and Behavioral Problems" (working Paper, Office of Applied Studies, Substance Abuse and Mental Health Services Administration, United States Department of Health and Human Services, 2000).

3. Nicole Avena, Pedro Rada, and Bartley Hoebel, "Evidence for Sugar Addiction: Behavioral and Neurochemical Effects of Intermittent, Excessive Sugar Intake," *Neuroscience & Biobehavioral Reviews* 32 (2008): 20–39.

4. Jennifer P. Schneider, "The Impact of Compulsive Cybersex Behaviours on the Family," *Sexual and Relationship Therapy* 18 (2003): 329–354.

5. Andreas G. Philaretou, Ahmed Y. Mahfouz, and Katherine R. Allen, "Use of Internet Pornography and Men's Well-Being," *International Journal of Men's Health* 4 (2005): 149–169.

CHAPTER 12

Nature

When I lived in the Philippines, I had many opportunities to enjoy that country's natural beauty. It's surrounded by water and blessed with regular, heavy rainfall during more than half the year, so the vegetation of the islands is luxuriant. But I was often reminded of the consequences of environmental pollution.

I worked for the Adventist International Institute of Advanced Studies, a General Conference-run university near Manila that meets the postgraduate needs of the church in Asia. The university's physical plant was developed based on a good master plan; consequently, its landscaping is beautiful, with healthy lawns and mature coconut trees nicely laid out among good-quality buildings of uniform style. There is, however, an ongoing environmental problem. The refuse dump of the nearby town is on the east side of the university property, separated from the campus only by a river.

The dump could have been a well-managed site where waste is received, sorted, and the organic materials covered with fresh soil every day. Instead, mixed garbage is simply piled there without any further processing. This results in offensive odors, a proliferation of flies, and clouds of smoke when the methane produced by the garbage catches on fire.

In my stint as president of the university, I took this matter seriously and attempted to negotiate at all levels, from the site scavengers all the way up to the person who was the country's secretary of environment and natural resources. We didn't seek to have the dump moved, although that would have been nice, but merely to have it run as the law prescribes. Our complaints occasionally halted its operation, but the activity always resumed a few weeks later with only minimal improvement. As far as I know, the problem still persists.

This is just a minute example of the continual environmental violations for which we are all to blame. From the simple example of an individual disposing of batteries improperly to a large factory throwing chemical waste into a river, human beings have subjected this earth to much maltreatment. As a result, what was meant to be a healthy and pleasant environment is now a threat to humanity.

God gave the earth and its natural resources to humankind. He meant His gift to reveal Himself, His love, and His character. He has shown mercy in preserving a great deal of the natural wealth and beauty He originally created—nature still provides life and enjoyment. But we human beings haven't always used what God has given us well. We've badly strained the natural functions of the earth. As a result, we witness air pollution, water contamination, noise contamination, greenhouse gas emissions, deforestation, reduction of habitats for wild animals, dumping of nuclear waste, the leaking of fertilizers into earth's rivers and seas, depletion of fish reserves, and more. We have yet to discover many of the consequences of disrupting and depleting nature, but we know some of them: new diseases plaguing humans and animals; deterioration of water quality; losses in agriculture, forestry, animal husbandry, and fisheries; the disastrous effects of climate change; and more.

However, while nature has deteriorated because of sin and human intervention, it still is a source of life and comfort to earth's inhabitants. It still contributes to our mental and physical health. It can still draw us to the Creator and thus enhance our spiritual health.

A perfect environment

Genesis 2 describes the Garden God planted in Eden—the place He made as a home for the first human beings. It contained trees of all kinds, which were a source of beauty as well as of food. Scripture doesn't describe the diversity of fruits, but considering the great variety that exists today, we can infer what that garden must have contained. The tree of life was there to be the source of perfect health, happiness, and endless life. And the tree of the knowledge of good and evil represented the limits set by the Creator. In addition to the streams of water coming up from the earth, the

Garden was watered by four rivers that moved across lands that contained great mineral resources—gold, aromatic resin, and onyx. Surely, there must have been many other things not mentioned, probably because the Garden was beyond description.

When God created Adam and Eve in His own image, He placed them in the Garden and told them to take care of it. With a divine genetic endowment and a glorious environment, the first couple had the optimal conditions for enjoying absolute happiness and perfect mental, physical, and spiritual health. They knew nothing of uncertainty, anxiety, and worry. Ellen White described their environment in this way:

> In the garden that God prepared as a home for His children, graceful shrubs and delicate flowers greeted the eye at every turn. There were trees of every variety, many of them laden with fragrant and delicious fruit. On their branches the birds caroled their songs of praise. Under their shadow the creatures of the earth sported together without a fear.
>
> Adam and Eve, in their untainted purity, delighted in the sights and sounds of Eden. God appointed them their work in the garden, "to dress it and to keep it." Genesis 2:15. Each day's labor brought them health and gladness, and the happy pair greeted with joy the visits of their Creator, as in the cool of the day He walked and talked with them. Daily God taught them His lessons.[1]

Touched by sin

The first two chapters of Genesis tell of God's wonderful creative power and the perfect happiness in Eden. But chapter 3 changes the tone. It presents the Fall and the array of awful consequences for Adam and Eve and the entire human family that resulted. Genesis 3:17, 18 tells us some of what sin has done to creation:

- *The ground was cursed.* Outside Eden, Adam and Eve encountered immediate barriers to working the soil—the ground started to produce weeds, thorns, and thistles, and no doubt other pests hindered healthy growth. Working hard sometimes didn't pay because the land and the weather weren't perfectly reliable any longer.
- *Human beings began to experience fatigue.* It seems that before the Fall, work produced the positive effects of physical activity

without causing tiredness. After sin, Adam and Eve experienced a totally new, painful sensation, which must have changed their attitude toward work and activity.

- *The original diet was changed.* In the beginning, the fruit from the trees and seed-bearing plants and from the tree of life provided perfect nourishment (Genesis 1:29; 2:16). After the Fall, " 'plants of the field' "(Genesis 3:18)—which, according to Genesis 1:30, were originally reserved for the animal kingdom— were added to the diet to compensate for the loss of the fruit from the tree of life.

Sin had many other effects upon the newly created world too. It may well have damaged the environment. Certainly, it changed the behavior of the animals and human beings. The animals began to kill each other for food and to exert their power. And hatred, jealousy, selfishness, and arrogance caused people to become aggressive toward each other and toward the animals. As described in Genesis 3–6, corruption and violence became so common that God was sorry He had made earth's creatures and people (Genesis 6:6, 7).

Paul affirms that nature is a victim of the sins human beings commit, but he offers hope for change. "The creation was subjected to frustration, not by its own choice, but by the will of the one who subjected it, in hope that the creation itself will be liberated from its bondage to decay and brought into the glorious freedom of the children of God. We know that the whole creation has been groaning as in the pains of childbirth right up to the present time" (Romans 8:20–22).

Though the earth has suffered a profound transformation, God has provided ways by which the human family may be protected from the adverse effects of the damaged environment. He tells us, " ' "If you follow my decrees and are careful to obey my commands, I will send you rain in its season, and the ground will yield its crops and the trees of the field their fruit" ' " (Leviticus 26:3, 4).

In His love and mercy, God preserved a large part of the original environment and plenty of natural blessings. When Paul and Barnabas were mistaken as gods by the inhabitants of Lystra and Derbe, Paul pointed instead to the true God, the Creator of heaven and earth and sea, along with everything they contain, who, he said, " 'has shown kindness by giving you rain from heaven and crops in their seasons; he provides you with plenty of food and fills your hearts with joy' " (Acts 14:17). The bounty of physical and psychological blessings nature can still convey is a source of life and happiness that our loving God has given us to compensate for the misery caused by sin.

Custodians of resources

Very early in my life, I was taught that whenever I visited someone and they offered me food or sweets, I was to thank them, smile, and take just a small portion of what they offered—and I was *never* to take seconds. The rationale had nothing to do with health or temperance but with ownership. In effect, my mother was saying, "Those sweets aren't yours. You can have them at home, but you mustn't abuse your neighbor's goodwill." Well, the truth was that we didn't have those sweets at home. Nevertheless, I wasn't to devour what wasn't mine, what belonged to my neighbor. Mother wanted me to care for the resources of others even more than I cared for my own things.

God hasn't given us the earth and its resources. They still belong to Him (Psalm 24:1). Some people think that as long as they have the money to pay for the fuel or food they want to consume, they can use up as much of it as they please whether they need it or not. They're free to ignore how much of the supply they're depleting. However, it's important that we remember that from the very beginning, the role of human beings has been to work on this earth and to take care of it (Genesis 2:15).

God has entrusted to us all the resources this earth contains, asking us to manage them wisely (Genesis 1:28). That is why the Israelites were given the instruction—still relevant today—to be frugal. If, for instance, an Israelite found a bird's nest, he or she wasn't supposed to take both the mother and the fledglings—just one or the other (Deuteronomy 22:6). The Israelites were also expected to care for the earth, for the poor, and for the wild animals. They were to do this, in part, by leaving the land unplowed and unused every seventh year and the vineyards and olive groves untended (Exodus 23:10, 11).

Humankind's stewardship extends to the animals. From early on in Scripture, animals are presented as sources of support for human beings. God has entrusted humans, as higher-order beings, with the responsibility of protecting the animals and using them wisely.

The Bible portrays cattle, goats, donkeys, sheep, mules, and horses as providers of work, food, clothing, transportation, and support for warfare. Also, they are used as the quiet victims of sacrifice—their death being a shadow of the cost and pain of Christ's supreme sacrifice.

Animals are not only helpers but also companions. This familiarity is depicted with Adam's naming each animal (Genesis 2:19). Human beings and animals lived together, worked together, and shared the discomfort of hardship and fatigue. With the coming of sin, the animals also seem to become corrupt: "for *all flesh* [human beings and animals] had corrupted his way upon the earth. And God said unto Noah, The end of all flesh is come before me" (Genesis 6:12, 13, KJV; emphasis added). We also find animals in the ark, sharing space with human beings so they, too, could be saved from the Flood.

And after the Flood, God established a covenant not only with Noah and his descendants, but also " 'every living creature that was with [him]— the birds, the livestock and all the wild animals' " (Genesis 9:10). And God's plan for the ultimate happiness of the inhabitants of earth includes animals as well as the human family. Isaiah 11:6, 7 portrays wolves, lambs, leopards, goats, cows, oxen, lions, bears, and their young pasturing together in peace under the leadership of a little child.

Caring for all entrusted resources is a serious responsibility that entails serious consequences. The Bible specifically says that the time of " 'wrath has come' "—the time to judge small and great—and " 'for destroying those who destroy the earth' " (Revelation 11:18). Certain scholars believe the term *the earth* as used in this apocalyptic message refers symbolically to the people of God, the saints. But surely the text extends beyond this narrow interpretation and can be understood also as condemning those who purposely damage God's creation.

The blessings of nature

Ecopsychology is a new field of study that involves observing how nature and natural surroundings produce positive effects on persons. Most results imply that the people who are healthiest are those who to stay close to nature and who use natural elements to improve their mood and to gain physical strength and comfort. Those who follow this approach recommend that when people can't go to nature, they bring nature to their home or work environment.

Jolanda Maas and her colleagues at the Netherlands Institute for Health Services Research in Utrecht, Holland, gathered data from 250,782 men and women regarding the relationship of people's proximity to green spaces and the state of their health.[2] Researchers working through general practitioners' offices (every Dutch person is assigned to a practitioner) were able to obtain data on twenty-four medical conditions of a physical and/or mental nature. In fifteen of the twenty-four, people's health was significantly better when they lived within half a mile of parks and woods. Those who lived a mile and a half or more from green space had poorer health. The correlations were strongest in the cases of mental disorders such as anxiety and depression and also among people who spent more time at home (for instance, children and the elderly). Possible explanations for these results include the beneficial effects of natural sunlight (more vitamin D), fresh air, exercise opportunities, and the whole sensorial interaction with a natural environment. These results remind us that God made people to function best in a natural environment.

Jules Pretty and his associates at the University of Essex, England, are involved in ongoing experimental research to ascertain the effects of various natural environments and conditions upon physical and mental health.[3] Among other benefits, they have found that exercise in nature causes significant improvements in self-esteem and various other measures of mood, as well as a decrease in blood pressure. Other studies are finding that (1) mental disorders are increasing because increasing numbers of people are living in cities, (2) hospital patients recover from illness more quickly when they can see nature from their beds, (3) counseling is more effective when the treatment plan includes time spent in nature—for example, in therapy gardens, horticultural therapy, or wilderness trips, (4) office workers suffer less stress when they can see greenery through their windows, and (5) people using computers can react more quickly when there are plants in their environment.

Foods made from plants and herbal medicines are among the greatest gifts God has given humanity. Plants—their fruits, seeds, leaves, and roots—provide the best way to prevent all sorts of illness and to cure many of them when they do occur. For generations, people in many parts of the world have been able to find remedies in products of the soil. Many have been medically tested. The natural products branch of the National Cancer Institute, for example, has been studying more than fifty thousand plant samples from around the world.[4] Through contracts with the Missouri Botanical Garden, the New York Botanical Garden, the University of Illinois at Chicago, the Arnold Arboretum of Harvard University, and the Bishop Museum in Honolulu, scores of plants and marine algae are being studied in the hope of finding a solution to the problem of cancer.

Blessings to curses

Blessings can turn into curses if we don't provide the necessary care and maintenance. The beautiful rice terraces of Banaue, Bontoc, and other villages in Ifugao Province in the northern Philippines form not only a gorgeous landscape but also a perfect ecosystem, where walls serve as dikes, and irrigation and drainage can be precisely regulated so the farmers can produce a high-quality crop. The system is also a social unit in which every farmer has to practice diligence and in which all have to exert collective discipline to manage the water and the soil. This rice terrace system has preserved the small agrarian unit, protecting the land from the heavy plough, the use of machinery, and the macroexploitation of the land with all its subsequent problems.

But the magnificent rice terraces of Ifugao Province are at risk of disappearing. Why? Visitors from near and far have discovered the indescribable beauty of these cultivated slopes and are flocking to see the marvel—and the locals have discovered that they make more money by setting up little stands and selling snacks and souvenirs to the tourists than they do by cultivating the terraces. So, many of the local people are abandoning their farming to attend to the tourists. They don't seem to realize that by neglecting the terraces they are destroying them, and that when the terraces are gone, the tourists will also disappear. Stories like this remind us that we need to discover what we're doing that's good for our environment and to find out what else we need to do to maintain it and improve it.

Beyond providing us with food, medicine, and recreation, natural environments also enable us to know God better. Nature helps us to see Him. It reminds us of the true Source of our blessings.

> God made the earth by his power;
>> he founded the world by his wisdom
>> and stretched out the heavens by his understanding.
> When he thunders, the waters in the heavens roar;
>> he makes clouds rise from the ends of the earth.
> He sends lightning with the rain
>> and brings out the wind from his storehouses (Jeremiah 10:12, 13).

Scriptures like this tell us not only of the wonderful balance still present in nature but also of God's character—that He's a caring Father who created heaven and earth and sustains the entire creation.

The example of Bible characters reminds us that nature can even improve our encounters with God through prayer and meditation. We see

Isaac going "out to the field one evening to meditate" when his father's servant had gone to search for a wife for him (Genesis 24:63). We read that John the Baptist went to the desert of Judea to commune with God before and during his ministry (Matthew 3:1). And, of course, on many occasions we are told of Jesus praying in the wilderness or in solitary places, for He "often withdrew to lonely places and prayed" (Luke 5:16).

You may live in an urban setting where you lack the godly influence of creation, or perhaps you live in the midst of nature but are so accustomed to the natural environment that it no longer makes you think of the Creator. Another look at Psalm 104 may help you to see the balance of forces in the wilderness and God's love for everything He made. Inspired by such an account, offer a prayer of praise to the Lord and thank Him for everything He has done to give life to His creatures. Repeat several times the words of Psalm 19:1, 2, "The heavens declare the glory of God; and the firmament sheweth his handywork. Day unto day uttereth speech, and night unto night sheweth knowledge" (KJV).

---

1. Ellen G. White, *The Ministry of Healing* (Mountain View, Calif.: Pacific Press®, 1942), 261.

2. Jolanda Maas et al., "Green Space, Urbanity, and Health: How Strong Is the Relation?" *Journal of Epidemiology and Community Health* 60 (2006): 587–592.

3. For reports on research by Jules Pretty, visit http://www.essex.ac.uk/bs/staff/pretty/green_ex.shtm.

4. National Cancer Institute and National Institutes of Health, "Natural Products Branch," Developmental Therapeutics Program, NCI/NIH, http://dtp.nci.nih.gov/branches/npb/repository.html.

CHAPTER 13

Partnership With Jesus

God sent Otilia to my family to give us the opportunity to know Jesus better. My family consisted of my mother, my grandfather, my sister, and me.

Otilia, a Seventh-day Adventist from my father's hometown, visited us before and after my father's death. She talked to us about answered prayers, the blessings of the Sabbath, and the delight of having a close friendship with Jesus. From the time my sister and I were toddlers, she invited us to church, but my mother was indifferent and for years courteously turned down the invitation. Nevertheless, we respected Otilia because of her kindness, sincere religious fervor, and her knowledge of the Bible.

Thanks to Otilia's persistence, when my sister and I were teens, our family began to visit the Seventh-day Adventist church and became interested in its doctrines. I struggled with some of the beliefs, but Otilia wasn't a dogmatic woman. She told me, "It isn't up to me to convince you of what is true and what isn't. Pray to God and ask Him to lead you in the right way. Pray with all your heart, and sooner or later He will answer. Then, do whatever He tells you."

My grandfather, then in his nineties, and my sister were baptized first. About a year later, my mother and I followed. The internal struggle I went through served to help me develop an intimate relationship with God, to depend on prayer, and to realize that God guides, leads, and blesses if we want Him to. For the first time in my life, I had a constant prayerful attitude about the choices I was making. Since then, I've had many opportunities to relate intimately with Jesus. This relationship has brought me the assurance of His presence and an incomparable peace of mind.

The blessing that comes from abiding in Jesus is not only spiritual, but physical and emotional as well. A growing body of research is showing that factors such as religiosity, faith, spirituality, prayer, forgiveness, hope, and church attendance are positively connected to health. After generations of calling religion the opiate of the people and blaming religion for some of the obsessions people had, science is admitting that a strong relationship with God is good for people's minds and bodies. When I got my psychology degree thirty years ago, no professional papers were read or studies conducted about prayer, religion, or spirituality. Now, any professional conference in the field will include a sizeable list of presentations on these topics, most of them reporting beneficial effects.

The Bible abounds in passages depicting believers as joyful—as having an authentic joy that comes from Jesus Christ. This doesn't mean that Christians don't experience pain. Rather, it means that they have an overflow of happiness that comes from above and enables them to handle trouble because of Jesus' grace. His life is the supreme example of spiritual connection with the Father.

Abiding in Jesus Christ, being in intimate connection with Him is the way to foster spiritual growth, well-being, and happiness. This chapter points to Him as the source of authentic happiness and as an example of how to live a joyous life in a world filled with pain and suffering. In the rest of this chapter I'll discuss the pathways that lead dependably to a joyful life—prayer, meditation on Scripture, worship, the practice of forgiveness, service to others, hope, and trust in God.

An individual relationship with Jesus

Mark 1:21–38 pictures for us one Sabbath that Jesus spent at Capernaum. He taught in the synagogue first thing in the morning, impressing the people by His authoritative words. He cast out a demon; and then, after the service, He, together with James and John, went to Peter's home. Finding that Peter's mother-in-law was ill, Jesus healed her. Then, at sundown, the whole town gathered at the door, bringing "all the sick and demon-possessed," and Jesus healed them all from their various diseases and drove out all the demons (verse 32). What happened after such a seemingly exhausting Sabbath day? Jesus got some sleep, and "very early in the morning, while it was still dark, Jesus got up, left the house and went off to a solitary place, where he prayed" (verse 35).

Jesus showed us how necessary it is for us to develop a good relationship with the Father. He approached God regularly in spite of the heavy demands His ministry made of Him. Doing so soothed Him and brought Him the physical, mental, and spiritual strength with which to face each day.

Like Jesus, we may also be subject to multiple pressures from work, family, health, and finances, but communion with Jesus will free us from such burdens. To me, interacting with Him involves the two processes of communication: I speak to Jesus through praise, prayer, sharing what I feel, and so forth; and He speaks to me through the Bible, counsel that others give to me, and impressions that come to me in moments of reflection. (I tend to do more speaking than listening. I admit that I need to do more of the latter!)

Counselors use guided imagery to help people with a variety of mental disorders. For example, a client who suffers from stress may be invited to imagine herself gazing at a beautiful coastal scene, feeling the warm, soothing breeze, and hearing the sound of seagulls. She can imagine the scent of the seawater and see herself walking in peace and calmness on the soft, sandy beach. She may also see herself walking into the temperate water, remaining there for a few moments, and then emerging and feeling the warmth of the sun on her skin. In order to increase my motivation to learn more about Jesus, at times I practice this kind of guided imagery as I meditate on passages in the Gospels. I find that doing so expands my understanding of those passages and gives the messages they contain great impact.

When using guided imagery, we should begin by asking God for guidance in our meditation. And we can find help in good commentaries that magnify Scriptures. Take, for example, the story of Levi-Matthew as told in Matthew 9:9–17. Read it together with the commentary Ellen G. White has provided in chapter 28 of *The Desire of Ages*. We can then think of the role publicans held in occupied Palestine. They weren't merely tax collectors for the foreign empire—they were also considered to be traitors who were taking advantage of their own people. We can imagine the thoughts and facial expressions of Matthew when Jesus approached him at his booth and invited him to be His disciple. We can envision the disapproval of the teachers of religion, who would consider this choice to be highly offensive. We can draw a mental picture of the party to which Matthew, excited about his new discipleship, invited his fellow publicans and other people of doubtful reputation to come and meet Jesus. We can think of the hopeful and tender messages Jesus might have given from His seat of honor amid this disreputable crowd. We can speculate on how His words might have stirred some of those present to make great changes in their lives. We can imagine all of this in colorful and vivid terms, observing Jesus displaying His godly character as He dealt with these outcasts. Then we can apply the story to our own experience—examining the shameful side of our lives and seeing Jesus as He smiles, forgives, and receives us just as He received them.

Corporate relationship with Jesus

A community of believers provides the spiritual support we need as we relate to Jesus—it provides the environment in which we can grow spiritually while maintaining mental balance and health. Marilyn Baetz, MD, is a member of the Department of Psychiatry at the University of Saskatchewan. She and her associates conducted a community health survey in Canada.[1] Over a period of seven months, they obtained data from thirty-seven thousand participants ranging in age from fifteen to the end of life. They gathered information about the prevalence of mental disorders, worship frequency, and spiritual values. Their research revealed a high but negative correlation between the two variables under study—mental disorders (depression, mania, panic disorder, and social phobia) and church attendance. This means that the higher the frequency of worship attendance, the fewer incidences there were of mental illness. These results may be interpreted as saying either that mental disorders may prevent people from going to church or that going to church may safeguard people from developing mental disorders—but the latter conclusion is just as likely as the former one.

Jeff Levin, a senior research fellow at the National Institute for Healthcare Research, conducted an analysis of hundreds of studies on the religion-health connection.[2] He found evidence that belonging to a religion was a protective factor against twenty-five illnesses or conditions, that it reduced the risk of dying from twenty-six named diseases, and that it protected against death from thirty-one types of cancer. The protected populations were from the following religious groups: Amish, Buddhist priests, Catholic nuns, Hindus, Hutterites, Jains, Jews, Latter-day Saints, Muslims, Parsis, Seventh-day Adventists, and Trappist monks.

A *National Geographic* study of longevity identified five groups of people who live significantly longer, healthier lives in comparison with the rest of their fellow citizens.[3] Four of the groups are ethnic and one is a religious group—Seventh-day Adventists in Loma Linda, California.

Why does belonging to a religious group make people healthier and happier? Experts have offered some suggestions.

- *Religion tends to promote a healthy lifestyle.* Many religions discourage the use of alcohol and other psychoactive substances, emphasize the importance of diet and exercise, and disapprove of promiscuous sexual behavior—presenting marriage and family life as God's ways. They also promote moderation in all things as a way to honor God.
- *Religion provides a suitable social network.* Most congregations offer a platform where people meet and develop supportive friendships. These people help others and are helped in turn when needs arise. Both clergy and members may provide formal and informal counseling, and many activities will be done in concert with people of common faith and values who care for each other.
- *Religion provides spiritual support.* Many religious groups offer worship, meditation, the study of sacred writings, and other spiritual activities in groups. This contributes to the edification of the community and the general well-being of members. Prayer is practiced individually and communally and is offered for those facing illness or hardship.
- *Religion teaches hopeful and trusting attitudes.* People of faith tend to have hope for better things in this life and beyond. They are likely to trust God and to live in a less stressful way, for they believe that Someone is in control of their lives. Thus, believers can cope better with their losses—illness, accident, death of a dear one, and so on—than can those with no religious hope.
- *Religion emphasizes the use of prayer and meditation.* Evidence shows that prayer and meditation are beneficial to various organic systems. Herbert Benson, a professor and researcher at Harvard University School of Medicine, studied the effects of prayer on the human organic systems and concluded that prayer slows down one's metabolism, reduces the cardiac rate, reduces the rate of breathing, amplifies brain-wave frequency, reduces blood pressure, causes feelings of internal calm, and improves general health.[4]

In addition to the benefits of mental and physical health that religion provides, there are also plenty of spiritual blessings for those who worship together in truth. It is risky to choose not to go to church, even for those who intend to remain loyal to God's principles away from the church community. Two or three Adventist families who were members of my church in Spain became disenchanted with the church organization and decided not to attend our local church anymore. "We'll still worship on the Sabbath and live as Adventists," they said. "But we can't continue to attend a church where the leaders aren't truly God's servants."

Some church members kept in touch with these families, and, yes, at the beginning they were worshiping in nature or in the homes of various members of their group. But, as the months went by, they became erratic in their meetings, and eventually, they quit worshiping and left the faith. Pastors and church members tried to bring them back, to no avail. They had left the support that the community of believers—albeit imperfect—provided. Unfortunately, this kind of thing has happened in many churches around the world.

Stable corporate worship provides the ideal, safe setting in which God can influence us. David must have been convinced of this, for he prayed,

One thing I ask of the LORD,
    this is what I seek:
that I may dwell in the house of the LORD
    all the days of my life,
to gaze upon the beauty of the LORD
    and to seek him in his temple (Psalm 27:4).

We are told that Jesus "went to Nazareth, where he had been brought up, and on the Sabbath day he went into the synagogue, *as was his custom. And he stood up to read*" (Luke 4:16; emphasis added). "Happy is the family who can go to the place of worship on the Sabbath as Jesus and His disciples went to the synagogue."[5]

Other factors in mental health

The Bible also insists on a number of attitudes and practices that cause spiritual, emotional, and physical well-being. All of them are related to our closeness to Jesus.

Forgiveness. We are hurt deeply when someone dear inflicts pain on us. Quite often, offenses come from a spouse, parent, child, sibling, friend, fellow church member, or coworker—the very people who can bring the most joy to our lives. Wounds made by these people can produce anger, bitterness, hatred, and the desire for revenge—highly negative feelings that undermine our mental and spiritual health. Turning instead to the pathway of Christian forgiveness brings us peace, joy, and closeness to God. That's why Paul encouraged the Colossian church to "bear with each other and forgive whatever grievances you may have against one another" (Colossians 3:13).

Mark S. Rye and his associates at the University of Dayton, Ohio, studied 199 people who had gone through divorce and belonged to community singles organizations.[6] The focus of this study was the effect forgiveness of the ex-spouse had upon the well-being of the subjects. The study found that forgiveness had a positive association with well-being—in other words, those who forgave their former spouse enjoyed greater well-being than those who didn't. Forgiveness was also inversely associated with depression and anger. In other words, the less forgiveness the subjects showed to their ex-spouses, the more depression and anger they experienced.

Forgiveness consists of letting go of adverse feelings and thoughts about the offender. We can truly forgive only with the support of God's Holy Spirit, since hatred and revenge seem to be natural human reactions when someone causes us pain. In addition to the spiritual blessings that come with forgiveness, it also brings about more satisfactory relationships, less hostility and stress, and less likelihood of developing anxiety and depression. In addition, it can lower our blood pressure and reduce the risk of our using and abusing substances.

Service. An important part of many treatment plans for depression is a realistic activity program with which the depressed person can fill his or her time. Counselors almost always include doing something profitable that also benefits someone else, as this has been found to work well in dissipating depressed moods.

Jesus spent a lot of time helping others. Scripture says He went " 'around doing good and healing all who were under the power of the devil, because God was with him' " (Acts 10:38). So, in fact, doing something to help others is not only a source of well-being, but also evidence that we are following in the Master's steps. And in the final judgment, it will speak to our salvation. " 'The King will say to those on his right, "Come, you who are blessed by my Father; take your inheritance, the kingdom prepared for you since the creation of the world. For I was hungry and you gave me something to eat, I was thirsty and you gave me something to drink, I was a stranger and you invited me in, I needed clothes and you clothed me, I was sick and you looked after me, I was in prison and you came to visit me" ' " (Matthew 25:34–36).

Trust. In a recent article, theologian Jürgen Moltmann, professor emeritus at the University of Tübingen, wrote,

> In the sad old days of the Soviet Union, everyone was able to marvel over the socialist police-state already at its very frontier. Having finally, after prolonged effort, acquired a visa and, after presenting a multiplicity of documents, one had to show one's passport to not just one official but, as a rule, four. The first official checked whether the visa was correct and the passport still valid and properly stamped; the second official checked that the first one had checked correctly; the third checked the second; and the fourth, finally, had to check the third, second, and first officials. The precept of Vladimir Lenin (1870–1924) ruled supreme: Trust is good but control is better.[7]

For our relationship with God, Moltmann submits an alternative to Lenin's precept: "Control is good—trust is better."

Trust is the only way to face the bitter realities of life and the fear of future adversities. But our trust must be in God, not in human beings. The verse that's in the middle of the Bible contains this very message: "It is better to trust in the LORD than to put confidence in princes" (Psalm 118:9, KJV). We do well when we trust in God's promises both for every step of our daily lives and for salvation at the end of time.

Hope. When I was a boy, I had to work hard to get a toy or the pair of shoes of my choice. To obtain them, I had to do something or reach some standard. It could involve chores, grades, or the elimination of a bad habit. The waiting time was a time of hope. I would dream of the toy, and this dream would help me do the agreed-upon duty until I reached the goal. But once I had obtained what I had been dreaming of, I was left without a goal and thus without hope. I needed something else to hope for, so I would go to my mother and suggest some other toy. In very simple terms, I couldn't be satisfied with life until I had something to hope for.

Hope is an essential for health—both physical and mental. There is ample evidence that ill people who hope to get better experience a faster and better recovery than those who have little or no hope. In the spiritual realm, hope is even more powerful:

"Life will be brighter than noonday,
　　and darkness will become like morning.
You will be secure, *because there is hope;*
　　you will look about you and take your rest in safety" (Job
　　11:17, 18; emphasis added).

In addition to being a motive for behavior and a factor in health, hope is a core element of religious experience. This hope is not just for mere material things, but for eternal salvation—as Scripture promises repeatedly. God gives religious hope freely and lovingly to His children (2 Thessalonians 2:16). It produces joy, peace, and trust (Romans 15:13), and it is focused on the second coming of Jesus: it is the "blessed hope" that moves us to remain active in expectation of the "glorious appearing of our great God and our Savior, Jesus Christ" (Titus 2:13).

In his *Divine Comedy,* the famous Italian poet Dante Alighieri (1265–1321) attempts to describe various eschatological sites, including hell. A number of warnings and messages are posted at the gates of hell. One of the most prominent says, "ALL HOPE ABANDON, YE WHO ENTER HERE." Although Dante's picture of hell differs greatly from what the Bible tells us about that place, it's interesting to see that in his imagination, lack of hope is the worst thing we can face.

If you aim for a joyful and balanced life and wish to have total health even in the imperfection of this world, follow Jesus' suggestion, " 'Remain in me, and I will remain in you' " (John 15:4).

---

1. Marilyn Baetz et al., "How Spiritual Values and Worship Attendance Relate to Psychiatric Disorders in the Canadian Population," *Canadian Journal of Psychiatry* 51 (2006): 654–661.

2. Jeff Levin, *God, Faith, and Healing* (Hoboken, N.J.: John Wiley & Sons, 2001), 32.

3. Dan Buettner, "The Secrets of Long Life," *National Geographic* 208 (2005): 2–27.

4. Herbert Benson, *Timeless Healing* (New York: Scribner, 1996).

5. Ellen G. White, *Education,* 251.

6. Mark Rye et al., "Forgiveness of an Ex-Spouse: How Does It Relate to Mental Health Following Divorce?" *Journal of Divorce and Remarriage* 41 (2004): 31–51.

7. Jürgen Moltmann, "Control Is Good—Trust Is Better: Freedom and Security in a 'Free World,' " *Theology Today* 62 (2006): 465.